THE WINDMILLS
OF ENGLAND

THE WINDMILLS
OF ENGLAND

Rodney de Little

Colwood Press

Heckington, Lincolnshire. *The last remaining eight sailed windmill. Now in full working order.*

First edition (under the title *The Windmill Yesterday and Today*),
John Baker, London, 1972
Second edition, 1975
Third edition, Colwood Press, 1997

Published in Great Britain by Colwood Press Ltd., Sextons Cottage, Jolesfield, Partridge Green, West Sussex RH13 8JT

Frontispiece: Chute, Wiltshire. *A very unusual smock mill in an area with few windmills.* (Arthur H. Davis. Author's collection)

ISBN 0 952 9930 0 7

Designed by Adrian Hodgkins Design, Oxford
Typeset by White Horse Graphics, Charlbury
Produced by Book Packaging and Marketing, Silverstone
Reproduction by MRM Graphics, Winslow
Printed in the United Kingdom by Information Press, Eynsham
A CIP catalogue record for this book is available from the British Library

Contents

Cross-In-Hand

**Cross-in-Hand,
Sussex.** *A typical post
mill with tailpole fantail
and sheet metal covering
to the body. The last
windmill to work for
trade in Sussex, it
finished in 1969.*

I first entered Cross-in-Hand windmill in 1955. Some men were working in the nearby power mill and Mr Ashdown, the miller, was in the roundhouse. The sails were turning briskly in a nice easterly breeze, each flashing earthward in the afternoon sun, the shutters rattling and squeaking as they swished past the roundhouse and soared again into the sky. There were no other visitors about, for this was a place of work.

In the roundhouse, sacks were piled high, the air dusty and smelling of meal and grain. The massive timbers of the trestle were polished from the friction of the continual passage of sacks for more than a century, the sack chain hanging in readiness for its next load, gleaming polished steel in the subdued light.

The ladder was high and steep, the treads deeply worn and repaired in places. At its foot the wheels ran on an iron tramway, the motion of the mill causing them to rock back and forth, the patched and weakened state of the old tailpole allowing it to flex more than had once been the case, the oil-encrusted wheel bearings deeply worn from years of ceaseless rocking. From time to time a heavy gust hit, the mill lurching in response to the accelerating sails and the ladder wheels jerking violently sideways.

The once-white paintwork was old and faded, the rear of the mill thickly coated with layer upon layer of lead paint. Once over the threshold the motion of the mill was apparent. Below, the ground and roundhouse roof swung from side to side, the mill body swaying and creaking, a sudden gust twisting it violently about the post, a loud cracking sound emanating from the direction of the collar. The fan came into action with more cracks from the collar, the mill lurching in response as the structure caught up with the bending tailpole.

The mill had sunk due to broken side girts, the worn and polished old floor rising in a hump around the post. A sack of ground meal stood in a long shaft of sunlight, others standing around in readiness for their journey below. Overhead the tail stones sang, barley meal pouring dustily into the bin on the left. Beside the door was a small writing desk, the beams nearby bearing discoloured newspaper cuttings of events in the lives of local windmills.

On the stone floor the iron stone nut turned above the runner stone, its highly polished teeth flashing in the sunlight. Dust was in the air and motion all around. The mill had once had three pairs of stones, but the left-hand pair had been removed from the breast in order to reduce weight. Both side girts had been plated with girders and iron brackets abounded around rotten joints in the breast. Every part moved and creaked and heaved. I stood on one end of the crowntree and watched the countryside far below outside the opposite window. A small bush swayed back and forth in response to the motion of the sails. Another gust struck, the crowntree jerking round, the collar emitting violent cracks and the bush being snatched from one side of the window to the other.

Mr Ashdown came up and threw open a trapdoor. Someone attached sacks to the chain, the hoist came into action, the chain rattled and several sacks came up

Cross-in-Hand, Sussex. *The author, at the age of eleven, talking to the miller, Mr Ashdown.* (Photograph Capt. A.E. Large)

through the void. These were tipped into the bin and the trapdoor dropped with a thud, the others closing automatically.

On the bin floor the motion was like that of a ship at sea. The tail was the best part, the movement really noticeable, sun entering through the little window in the gable, the woodwork polished all around and the striking gear rising and falling in response to the gusting wind. Mounds of grain showed in the various bins, barley, wheat and oats for the oat crusher in the breast. Overhead, there hung the sack hoist bollard, while in the breast the brake wheel turned slowly, but with effortless power.

In such a place there is a sense of time, of all the generations who have led to this moment, of those who built the windmill, who worked it, who laboured in it for a modest wage and of farmers and gleaners who brought their grain and stood in this very spot.

This was the windmill at work.

CHAPTER I

The English Windmill

Grain has been ground for some thousands of years; first by hand in pairs of simple stones known as querns, later by horse or bullock power, and then by water power using a horizontal paddle wheel driving a vertical shaft.

It is not known when some bright individual conceived the idea of inverting the horizontal water mill and shielding one side of its paddle from the wind in order to create thrust on the other, but that was the moment of the conception of windpower. The horizontal windmill is still in use in some Middle Eastern countries, but while its arrangement seems neat, it also suffers from a number of inefficiencies, the most obvious being that only a small part of the total sail area is producing power at any given moment, whereas the sails of the vertical windmill are all contributing energy to the windshaft.

Arundel Cement Mill.
After completion in 1864. (Photographer unknown)

In order to produce a satisfactory vertical windmill, two major problems have to be solved: how to turn the sails to wind and how to divert the power from a horizontal drive to one that is vertical. The last is the most daunting, and gears the answer. It was the arrival of these that enabled the vertical windmill to be introduced.

There is fierce discussion between academics as to where and when the windmill as we know it was invented. For many years it was believed that they were seen in the Middle East by the Crusaders, or that they were first conceived in China. More recent research has indicated a European birthplace and some specifically point to Northern France. Whether any particular theory will ever be proven to be definitive is doubtful, for inventions have a tendency to evolve step by step and it is not impossible that the horizontal windmill was seen in the Middle East and the vertical windmill created for the more variable wind conditions of Europe, or even that the new power source arrived independently once the right-angled gear drive had been established.

The first windmills were of the post type, where the entire working structure is turned to face the wind. Illustrations date from around 1190 and show a very small structure of crude construction. Earlier written references exist and it is currently believed that the windmill had come into existence by the 1130s. There are earlier references to mills, but these were probably watermills, although some researcher may well locate some positive reference in a few years time and so push the origins back still further into the obscurity of time.

From the twelfth century the windmill spread through England and, to a limited extent, Scotland and Wales, until by the 1840s there were approximately

10,000 in existence. William Coles-Finch, in his book *Watermills and Windmills* (1933), traces more than 400 in Kent and there were probably equal numbers in Sussex and other eastern counties.

DISTRIBUTION

The watermill is fundamentally a shed that contains machinery. It does not have to turn to wind and neither does it have to make use of a light breeze but withstand a hurricane, and it can be built in a convenient place without consideration of trees or hills that might obscure its power source. For this reason it was usually built in preference to its complicated cousin, the windmill. Counties that have plenty of water with a reasonable fall tend to have fewer windmills, and for this reason the main development and concentration of windmills was in the east. Of the western counties, only Lancashire and Anglesey had windmills in any number, both areas creating their own distinctive style of mill.

Those areas that had many streams had very few windmills, although it is surprising how many windmill sites research tends to reveal. That great enthusiast from Shropshire, Peter Lewis, tells me that there were once as many as fifty windmills in his county.

Aldington, Kent. *The long-demolished mill in its working days.* (Collection of V. G. Pargeter)

DEVELOPMENT

While the windmill spread throughout Europe and as far afield as the Ukraine and the USA, its sophistication varied greatly. Holland is frequently regarded by those with limited knowledge as being Mecca for the windmill enthusiast, but in reality while there were many windmills in that country, these were not by any means all of a highly developed type and it can safely be said that nowhere else in the world was the windmill superior to those found in England. Not only was this ultimate development confined to a single, rather small, country, but within that country each of the three main types of windmill was advanced to its ultimate world peak within a particular county – Suffolk for the post mill, Kent the smock mill and Lincolnshire the tower mill.

DECLINE

The peak in windmill design roughly coincided with the steam engine beginning to provide its power to great mills at the ports. For many years the public had sought whiter and whiter bread, something unobtainable where any bran particles remain within the flour. The roller mill was the answer and this, coupled to predictable and massive steam power in buildings where grain could be loaded directly from barges or trains, and where economies of scale could outmatch the wind and watermill, rapidly drove the windmill from the vicinity of the major cities.

The railway train enabled flour to travel quickly from its place of origin and by 1895 windmill flour was declining fast, even the grist trade for cattle failing to hold the position of the windmill. Sails were removed, steam engines installed, mills demolished and by the time the motor lorry and the First World War had arrived, flour production was virtually extinct.

Shortage of timber for repair and government interference coupled with economic pressures caused many mills to cease work during The Great War, the aftermath of which was a period of decline heading into the depression of the 1930s.

In 1929 the Society for the Protection of Ancient Buildings, an organisation with its foundations in the Arts and Crafts movement of William Morris, started a windmill section. At last there was a realization that something of national, technical and aesthetic importance was being lost, grants being made to enable some mills to remain at work while publicity encouraged a new attitude towards preservation of what remained. By 1939 attitudes had changed sufficiently for the post mill at Stanton in Suffolk to be renovated to work again, but at the final moment the war intervened, the millwright left the site "to carry out war work", a second pair of sails was never fitted and the mill remained in this state until it was completely restored for work during the 1980s.

Severe economic times coupled with a shortage of timber once again caused many mills to cease turning. The late Rex Wailes recorded some twenty-three still at work in his book *The English Windmill* of 1953, although there were in fact twenty-four, for he missed Stelling Minnis mill in Kent.

At the start of the 1960s there were eight mills working and a number of county councils and other public bodies were concerning themselves with preservation of windmills that at least appeared reasonably complete. These restorations were mostly of the external shell, much historic machinery being destroyed and

Northbourne, Kent. *A rare sight, two windmills at work in the same village on the same day in the 1930s. Northbourne Old Mill (above left) and New Mill (above right).* (Photograph F.W. Gregory)

little regard being paid to historical accuracy of sails, boarding or any other part that was replaced. No thought was given to keeping the last few mills at work, nor of preserving other than the obvious, and several fine mills were lost, including Ash post mill in Kent which collapsed due to the failure of one joint while protracted negotiations were in progress and the collapse in 1961 of Outwood smock mill, one of a pair and arguably the largest smock mill in England.

THE NEW ERA

The mid 1960s saw the beginning of a new era. Interest was growing rapidly and groups of enthusiasts were beginning to undertake restorations that would never have been considered a few years before. Authenticity was at last being taken into account and as the 1970s arrived complete rebuilds began to occur.

Since the first edition of this book was published in 1972 there have been some remarkable changes in the situation of the English windmill. These changes encompass restoration, maintenance, rebuilding and even completely new traditional windmills. Twenty-odd years ago it would have been dismissed as wishful thinking to suggest that by the mid-1990s there would be around forty-five windmills grinding either regularly or occasionally. The person who forecast that it would be feasible once again to make a living by grinding flour by wind would have been dismissed as crazy and the individual who believed that 1994 would see sails on the empty tower of Asterly mill or sails up a few weeks earlier on the new smock mill at Leinthall Starkes would have been sent straight to the asylum!

But it has happened.

We live in a curious age. There are precise, computer-controlled machines that can turn out mechanical components for car engines that would once have employed armies of expert machinists. There are communications that allow the New York stock market to react to a drop on the Japanese market before the man in the street has eaten his breakfast. Everything is more exact and easier.

It is a paradox that while things are becoming less difficult and ever more precise, there are increasing numbers of people who appreciate things that are hand-made, slightly different, one from the other, and the result of individual skill. Not only do some people appreciate these things, but some have a desire to go against the trend of conformity and that which is ordinary and create something themselves. When they apply their effort and skill to restoring or building a windmill, the end result is not a static model in a glass case, but a living, vibrant machine which works differently in every wind and which mirrors so closely the elegance combined with practicality of the sailing ship.

Of course, the reaction against the sameness of modern existence is not confined to those who rebuild windmills. There is a vast interest in old-fashioned cars, steam engines, railways and wooden boats, and indeed, only a few days before writing this I heard that a group of enthusiasts is to build an exact copy of a lost type of steam railway locomotive, the first to be built for more than forty years! That the windmill restorer is not unique, but part of a more general movement is perhaps evidenced by the fact that I have a strong interest in motor cars of the 1920s and that Vincent Pargeter, the millwright, not only owns a pumping windmill, but is also restoring a magnificent sailing wherry.

Of the windmills that were working when this book was first written, only North Leverton and Alford can claim to have worked continually, although Outwood post mill has always been capable of work. Sadly, there are currently no post mills working for trade, the last, at Drinkstone Suffolk, having ceased some years ago on the death of Mr Clover, the miller. The windmills that are now working fall into three categories: those that run for the benefit of the public on a few open days during the year, those that are regularly open and have been "museumised", and those like Alford, Boston and Sarre, which are primarily working mills but which allow the public to look around as an additional source of income. To these could be added a small, but growing, fourth group of windmills like my own little post mill and the charming post mill at Stanton which was restored by the late Mr Richard Duke. Both these mills work regularly for the pleasure of their owners, but are not open to the public.

That there is a wide and apparently increasing level of interest is shown by there being no shortage of visitors even in the more unusual areas for tourists, like Lincolnshire. The interest of a more casual public is indicated by the fact that someone who owns a house near the site of Ashcombe mill, Lewes, told me that he is continually troubled by people asking for the whereabouts of the windmill – it was blown down in 1916!

Friston, Sussex.
Collapsed 1927.
Photographer unknown

Thorne, Yorkshire.
Note the small diameter roundhouse, roundhouse roof turning with the mill body and roller reefing sails. Two sails are fited with shutters on the leading side to give better regulation. (Detail from old postcard)

Bozeat, Northamptonshire.
A very unusual arrangement where the breast was extended to allow stones to be driven forward of the brake wheel. (F. W. Gregory, 1930s)

Left: **East Hoathly, Sussex.** *There was a tailpole fantail and sack slide hinged to the handrail. The mill burnt down in 1881.* (J. Seabrook. Old postcard)

Right: **Nyetimber, Sussex.** (Old postcard)

Far right: **Yardley, Warwickshire.** *Unusual treatment of the ogee cap, giving a very onion-like appearance.* (Old postcard)

Right: **Barking, Essex.** *The mill at work. Note the steeply battered tower.* (Photographer unknown)

Far right: **Haddenham, Buckinghamshire.** *The mill mentioned in* The Village Carpenter *by Walter Rose.* (Old postcard)

Part One

Windmill Design & Construction

Lowfield Heath, Surrey. *As it stood before renovation. The sails were dummies erected before the war.*

Chapter 2

Post Mills

The earliest type of windmill was the post mill. The post mill at Chillenden in Kent was built in 1868 to an earlier design, probably in order to reduce costs.

The entire square upper part of the structure is turned to face the wind, only the lower part, known as the trestle, remaining stationary. The body, or buck as it is called in East Anglia, is supported by a single huge centre post, twenty to twenty-two feet long and three or more feet thick at the base. Within the body lies the machinery, the whole movable part of the mill resting upon the crowntree, a massive timber with a bearing at the centre that runs from side to side of the mill and across the top of the post like the cross stroke of the letter "T". Access to the body is gained via the ladder which is of heavy construction and has the important additional duty of holding the mill steadily into the

Finchingfield Mill, Essex. *This sectional drawing, made by Vincent Pargeter when planning the restoration of the mill, demonstrates the basic structure and arrangement of a post mill.*

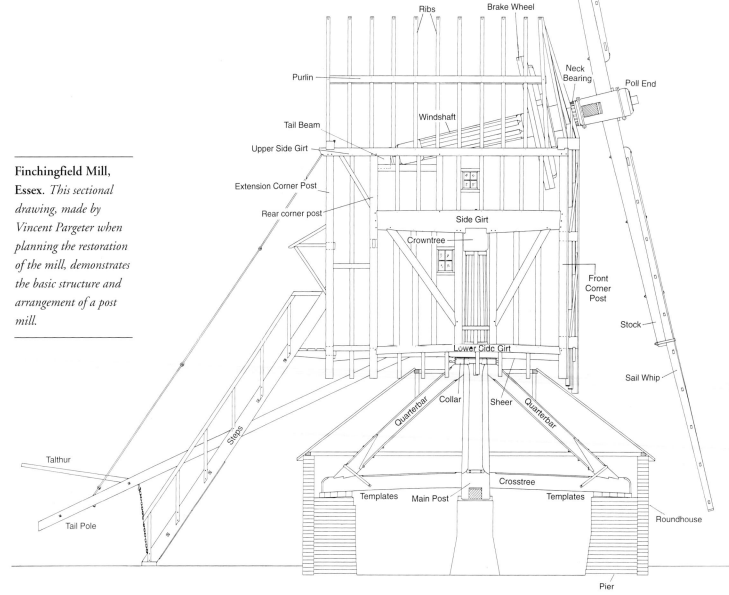

Right Side

Smarden, Kent. *The trestle of a post mill. This mill was blown down in the early 1950s.*

Chillenden, Kent. *An open trestle post mill that was turned to wind by means of a tailpole. This mill is not as old as it appears, having been built in 1868. Now preserved, but with much machinery removed and a nearby granary demolished.*

Above: **Ash, Kent**. *The horns of the main post. This mill was blown down in 1953.*

Above right: **Lowfield Heath, Surrey**. *The post entering the mill. The floor of the body can be seen with the sheer beams and collar encircling the post.*

Above: **Ash, Kent**. *Despite its age, an almost perfect tenon that once joined the quarter bar to the post and took one-quarter of the weight of the mill.*

Right: **Outwood, Surrey**. *The post inside the mill body. The crowntree passes across the top of the post. This is the spout floor. This mill is still in working order.*

wind and may even give some support during a hurricane.

The body is turned to wind by means of the tailpole, the ladder, which is hinged at the upper end, first being raised clear of the ground by means of the *talthur*, a wooden lever visible on the side of the tailpole in the photograph. This is pushed down and held in that position by a loose pin while the miller pushes the mill round to face the wind. Despite the weight being fifteen to twenty tons, the mill moves quite easily, the body being well balanced and the leverage from the tailpole considerable.

The sails turn the windshaft which passes well into the mill and is inclined downward at the tail, the machinery being driven from this by gearing.

If the reader refers to both the sectional drawing of Finchingfield Mill and to the photograph of Chillenden it will be possible to follow the sequence of construction. Photographs of details are indicated by the name of the mill. From the bottom upwards there are four brick piers upon which the *trestle* (Smarden, p.21) is supported. The trestle consists of two large cross-timbers supported at each end by the piers. These are known as the *crosstrees*. The crosstrees cross over one another at the centre and the main post rises above them. The post has four *horns* (Ash, above) which pass round the crosstrees and steady it at this point. Four *quarterbars* rise from the ends of the crosstrees and meet at the post just below the mill floor (Lowfield Heath). These quarterbars actually take the full weight of the mill, and no weight is taken on the centre of the crosstrees. There is, in fact, a small clearance at this point, and the weight passes from the post (Ash, right) down the quarterbars (Great Hormead) and directly through the crosstree ends on to the *piers*. The trestle is very strong, and the crosstrees and quarterbars are usually of oak and about one foot thick. The post is very substantial at the horns and is often as much as 3'6" thick; four feet has been mentioned, but I have never measured one quite so large.

The post passes up through the mill floor (Outwood) and sockets into the *crowntree* in the ceiling. The crowntree passes from side to side of the mill, and has a socket in the centre into which the *pintle* (Ash, opposite) of the post fits. The whole mill body turns on this point. The socket and pintle are normally of

Above left: **Great Hormead, Hertfordshire.** *The joint between the quarter bar and the crosstree. Note the bird's mouth joint with concealed tenon. This is a critical point in the structure of a post mill and its failure through neglect caused the loss of Ash, amongst other post mills.*

Above: **Ash, Kent.** *The iron pintle separated from its iron socket on the crowntree. The usual bearing was wood to wood, but this was often replaced with an iron samson head due to wear.*

Ash, Kent. *The joint between the crowntree (bottom) and side girt.*

Portland Bill, Dorset. *The windshaft hanging inside the tower. Note the wooden poll end, the iron bearing plates let into the shaft just below it, the mortices for a compass arm brake wheel half way down and the iron gudgeon pin at the bottom.*

wood, but sometimes these wear and are replaced with iron. This is known as the *samson head*. The crowntree is usually of oak and very large, being about two feet thick. The crowntree at Clayton post mill, Sussex, is built up of four pieces of pitch pine clamped and pegged together, and measures twenty-seven inches across. The post of this mill is also built up out of four pieces of pitch pine, a very unusual arrangement.

Where the post passes through the floor there is a steady bearing called the *collar*. The two *sheer beams* pass from front to rear one either side of the post, two smaller timbers join these fore and aft of the post forming a square collar around the post (Lowfield Heath, p.22). On either end of the crowntree are the *side girts* (Ash, above). Each takes half the weight of the mill and joins on to a *corner post* at either end. Above and below the side girts are the *upper* and *lower side girts* or *side rails*. The corner posts are joined front and rear by minor timbers, and it will be seen that the whole construction is very strong.

Across the top of the front (or breast) two corner posts rests the *breast beam*; this has the *chair block* at its centre which supports the neck bearing of the *windshaft*. Between the upper side girts at the rear is fitted the *tail beam*, which supports the *tail bearing* of the windshaft.

The sheer beams are very important, for apart from forming the collar they support the beams which in turn support the ladder at the rear; the tailpole is fitted to them also at the rear, and in the breast they support the upright post known in East Anglia as the *prick post*. The prick post supports the centre of the breast beam.

The windshaft on early mills was wooden and octagonal or round, and tapered from breast to tail. The tail bearing was a simple iron pin with iron fins like a bomb. These fins fitted into deep mortices in the tail of the shaft, leaving just the pin projecting. The result looked very similar to the pintle (Ash, p.23). The *neck* (Portland Bill) consisted of a number of iron strips let into the wooden shaft, and held with clamps at either end. This neck turned in the *neck bearing* which was a U-shaped wooden bearing in early mills, but later mills used a large brass bearing resting in an iron base. When Hildenborough Mill, Kent was pulled down (p.30) the neck bearing was found to be of wood, although the windshaft was a later iron example. The bearing was actually made up of about half a dozen pieces of wood bolted together and standing on edge with the "U" shape cut out for the windshaft.

In front of the neck bearing and outside the mill is the *poll end*. Here the windshaft is square and has two mortices passing through at right angles to one another. Through these pass the *stocks* which have a sail fitted on each end, and the stocks are held in the mortices in the poll end by wedges. These wooden poll ends often rotted after many years use, and were cut off and replaced by an iron poll end with fins, which fitted inside mortices in the wooden shaft like the tail bearing. These iron poll ends had the advantage of not rotting and of having a smooth iron neck, rather than the iron strips. An original wooden poll end could be seen at Gayton Mill, Cheshire (p.35) until recently, and an even more primitive one remains inside Portland Bill Mill, Dorset.

On the windshaft behind the neck is fitted the *brake wheel* (Nutley). This wheel is the largest wheel in the mill, and may measure up to ten feet across. Around the rim are the *gear teeth* which drive the *stone nut* which drives the stones. Around the perimeter of this wheel is the *brake* which is a ring of sections of wood which almost encircle the brake wheel. The brake is hinged at one end and has a

Nutley, Sussex. *The brake wheel, windshaft and stone nut. The wooden brake band is visible against the lower part of the rim.*

Stanton, Suffolk. *The bin floor with the top of the brake wheel and brake. The sack hoist with its chain drive and bollard may be seen in the roof.*

long, heavy lever attached at the other. The lever is held up by a catch while the mill is working, but can be gently released from any floor by a rope. The brake is very powerful, and has a "self wrapping" effect which causes it to tighten its grip under load. This must be used with care, for sudden release might well cause damage to a sail.

Early windmills had only one pair of stones in the breast, driven from the brake wheel; later mills had a *tail wheel* which drove another pair of stones in the tail. Early mills also had only two floors; the *stone floor* (at side girt level) and the *spout floor* (at collar level) and the grain supply was limited by the size of the hoppers immediately above the stones. Later mills had three floors with an extra floor at upper side-girt level to hold bins which contained a larger supply of grain for the stones than was previously possible (Stanton).

Balance is an important feature of all windmills, but especially of post mills. The post is placed forward of the centre line as can be seen on p.20. The object is to counter-balance the weight of the sails in the breast, and also the considerable weight of the stones, which can be one and a half to two tons when new. For the same reason the windshaft is inclined downwards at the tail. This brings the weight well back from the sails, and enables them to clear the crosstree ends. The windmill is designed to receive thrust from the breast only. If a working windmill is tailwinded it can draw the windshaft forward out of the tail bearing, and as the sails rush round backwards the windshaft creates havoc as it smashes the bins and interior. In a bad case the windshaft may be torn clean out of the mill, or the mill may be blown over forwards.

If the brake is on and the mill not running it would take a very strong tailwind to cause any damage, but it is an unwise miller who goes off to lunch and leaves the mill running unattended. The mill at Syleham, Suffolk (p.56) ended its working days with two sails only, due to a tailwind in the late 1940s. The wind suddenly changed through 180 degrees while the mill was at work, and the sails ran round backwards, drew out the tail bearing and, tipping the windshaft upwards, two sails dashed themselves to pieces against the mill. Eventually, two good sails and a stock were sorted out from the remains, and were on the mill until 1987. The post mill at Thornham Magna was once tailwinded too, and ended with a distinct forwards lean. While on this subject, it is as well to point out that a windmill can continue to work with two sails only, and that if one sail becomes damaged the opposite number can be removed and the mill remain at work.

Most post mills have the trestle enclosed in a *roundhouse* which provides storage space. Many later post mills are on very high brick piers. Friston Mill, Suffolk, is an example with high piers and a three-storey round house.

Friston, Suffolk. *The finest remaining post mill in the world, photographed in 1958. This represents the ultimate development of the windmill. The engine house against the roundhouse has since gone.*

CHAPTER 3

Smock Mills & Tower Mills

The *smock mill* was probably first used in this country during the seventeenth century, and is a rather more complicated type of mill than the post mill. The great difference between the two types is that only the *cap* with the sails and windshaft turns to face the wind. The tower stays stationary, and with it the machinery. The smock mill at Stelling Minnis, Kent, is a good example. Only the rectangular top or cap turns. This mill is fitted with an automatic device for turning the cap, known as the *fantail*; this keeps the cap facing the wind at all times. Early smock mills were turned to face the wind by means of a tailpole (West Wratting), but later ones, as at Henlow, Bedfordshire, and Shiremark, Surrey, were turned by means of an endless rope or chain which ran over a wheel and down to the ground in a loop. The miller pulled on one side or the other of the rope and

West Wratting, Cambridgeshire. *An old smock mill turned to wind by a tailpole. At the time there were two clockwise and two anti-clockwise sails fitted.*

Stelling Minnis, Kent. *A typical Kentish smock mill. Only the rectangular cap turns to face the wind and the octagonal tower remains stationary. A late mill built in 1866 on the site of a post mill. The last windmill to work in Kent, it ceased in the early 1970s.*

Hildenborough, Kent.
The framing of the tower and cap frame are clearly seen. The brick base is higher than is usual with a mill of this age and type. Demolished 1961.

Henlow, Bedfordshire.
The wheel-and-chain winding mechanism. The chain or rope is missing.

Henlow, Bedfordshire.
Like Hildenborough, this mill had wheel-and-chain winding or luffing gear. Compare this Midlands framing and cap shape with that of the South.

revolved the wheel. The wheel was connected by reduction gearing to a pinion which meshed with the teeth of the rack, which had a considerable number of teeth, and encircled the top of the tower of the mill. It will be seen that by winding the wheel round with the rope, the cap can gradually be moved to face the wind (Henlow). This device is known as *wheel-and-chain*, or *wheel-and-rope luffing gear*. An old type of smock mill at Hildenborough, Kent, was turned by a wheel-and-chain gear, and the wheel may be seen standing up at the rear of the cap. The sails and chain were reached from a gallery or stage, which has since fallen off. A much lower mill at Henlow, Bedfordshire, did not require a stage.

Caps varied greatly in shape, but the basic early design is similar to the rectangular type found on Kentish mills. The picture of Hildenborough shows the rectangular frame with the *cap sheers* running fore and aft on either side of the cap. The breast beam connects the sheers in the breast, and the tail beam does the same in the rear. Between the sheers, just to the rear of the brake wheel, is the *sprattle beam* which is over the centre of the tower.

Around the top of the tower is the *curb*, and the *rack* is fitted to the outside of this. The curb is usually of wood, but can be of cast iron, and the cap rests directly on this. There are three types of curb: *dead curb, live curb* and *shot curb*. The dead curb has the cap skidding round on well-greased brass or iron pads. The live curb has the cap running on iron rollers (Leigh) and the shot curb has a great number of small rollers. The dead curb is stiffest to turn, but is really preferred by most millers as it stays where it is resting, and does not yaw about. There is, however, considerably less resistance and greasing is required less frequently with the live curb. Some millwrights compromised by combining the two. Hildenborough was an example, for here there was a row of rollers under the breast beam, the heaviest part, and two large wheels with small bearings (these could not have taken much weight) at either end of the breast beam. The rest of the curb was dead.

The cap is centred by the *truck wheels* or centring wheels (Woodchurch) which run round the inner face of the curb. The truck wheels are very important, for any slackness in the fitting of the cap would alter the position of the brake wheel and the *wallower* (Stelling Minnis) which takes the place of the stone nut on the post mill. The wallower is mounted on the upright shaft which extends from the bearing at the sprattle beam in the cap to the stone floor several floors below. If the cap was too far off centre the upright shaft would not be vertical and the winding gears might not be in proper mesh with the rack.

Leigh, Kent. Bottom left: *The rollers upon which some caps turn. These run on the upper iron face of the curb. The remains of this mill collapsed in 1963.*

Woodchurch, Kent. Bottom centre: *The centring or truck wheels which run against the inner face of the curb to maintain the cap centrally on the tower.*

Stelling Minnis, Kent. Bottom right: *The wallower and upright shaft as seen from below. The lower part of the brake wheel is to the right with an iron brake band.*

Jolesfield, Sussex. *The dismantled cant posts showing the special tenon that linked the cills (top) and the tenon with the curb (bottom).*

Pakenham, Suffolk. *The great spur wheel and stone nut. Note the internal iron gear ring.*

The curb is supported by eight *cant* or *corner posts*, which slope upwards from the cills which rest on the top of the brick base. The slope or *batter* is of importance, as it gives the body or tower of the mill great rigidity. Between the cant posts is the diagonal bracing which keeps the tower rigid. The great failing of smock mills is the tendency of the tower to distort, the curb to become uneven or oval, and the cap to jam. A little decay in the joints can soon cause this trouble which, while easily cured with tie-rods and new timber where necessary, can be very tiresome. The brick base must be strong also, for this carries the cills which support the entire mill. The pressure at the cills is outwards as well as downwards, and when the cills are new they are joined at each corner, so that there is little sideways pressure on the walls of the base. If the cills are neglected and the joints weaken, the resultant outward pressure may soon crack a lightly built base. Sometimes iron bands are fitted around the base to try to remedy this fault (Willingham, p.114). Bases vary from a few courses in height, as at Stelling Minnis, to several floors, as at Cranbrook, Kent. They also vary in shape from octagonal to round or to square, and many Kentish mills were built on square bases, the cills crossing the corners diagonally. Not all smock mills were octagonal, variations ranged from round to six-sided. Square smock mills have been built, only as small drainage mills.

The upright shaft descends through the mill to the stone floor where it is supported by the *footstep bearing*. Just above the footstep bearing the *great spur wheel* is mounted (Pakenham). Around the rim of the great spur wheel are situ-

ated the stone nuts which drive the stones. Some later mills have the stones driven from beneath, in which case the upright shaft is longer, and the great spur wheel and stone nuts are situated below the stone floor.

The arrangement of floors in a smock mill varies greatly, but usually there is the brick base, which serves as a spout floor, the stone floor, the bin floor and, just beneath the cap, the dust floor. The advantage that a smock mill has over the post mill is that, although it is more complicated and more inclined to leak and so decay, it can be built to a greater height. Therefore, more pairs of stones can be driven from the increased wind available, and the size of sails can also be greatly increased to provide more power. Suffolk millwrights preferred post mills, and placed their mills on gigantic brick piers for the same reason.

Drinkstone, Suffolk. *A very interesting smock mill that is reputed to have been built on a horse mill that forms the wooden base. The sails of the post mill may be seen just showing in the distance.*

Horton Conquest, Bedfordshire. *A tower of unusual shape. The three doors, one above the other, have caused the tower virtually to split in two.*

Gayton, Cheshire. *A very old tower mill with wooden poll end and cap typical of the North-east. This is now unfortunately house-converted.*

Left: **Pakenham, Suffolk**. *The last tower mill to work by wind in the county. It has now ceased due to the death of the owner, Mr Bryant.*

The design of the *tower mill* is very similar to that of a smock mill, with the major exception that the wooden tower is replaced by one of brick or stone. Although tower mills were probably invented at the same time as smock mills, they did not become popular until a rather later date. Perhaps the answer lies in cost or the difficulty of constructing the tower. The great advantage of a tower mill is that the tower is leakproof (some mills had iron plates fitted to the weather side and others were tarred to assist this) and, unless very badly constructed, do not distort. Although most mills have the doors and windows in line all the way up, this is not a good thing as cracks can develop between them. The tower at Horton Conquest had no fewer than three doors above one another, and the result can be seen from the illustration; the tower is splitting into two halves. To repair this type of damage can be most difficult. The strange shape of some tower mills is due to the tower having been built on the brick base of a smock mill. This is not likely in the case of Horton Conquest, however, as the bricks seem contemporary.

The tower of the very old mill at Gayton is very short but strong, and is built from large red stone blocks. The cap of this mill is typical of Cheshire and Shropshire mills. The tower at Portland Bill (p.36) is typical of the South-west, with its vertical sides, and there are hardly any windows, so the mill must have been incredibly dark to work in. Vertical towers are not a good feature, as without a good batter there was a tendency to crack. The tower at Wendover (p.36) is nearly vertical, but has not cracked, probably aided by the strong construction and careful spacing of the windows. This is a very odd mill, as the tower is octagonal, and the huge cap is, to say the least, unusual in shape.

Portland Bill, Dorset.
A primitive vertical sided tower. The windshaft has fallen inside and is suspended from the stock.

The peak of the tower mill design was reached in Lincolnshire with immensely tall brick towers with beautiful ogee-shaped caps. The tops of some of these towers were corbelled out to a slightly greater diameter just below the curb. Burgh-Le-Marsh mill exemplifies the best Lincolnshire mills.

The machinery was identical to that of a smock mill, although with the exception of Kent, where smock mills were the speciality, tower mills were built last of all, and often had very modern iron machinery. The last was built at Much Hadham in Hertfordshire in 1892.

The latest type of cap was usually round in pattern, and some late mills like East Blatchington pumping mill, Sussex, copied the Lincolnshire cap. Round caps provide a better air-flow behind the sails, but suffer from being unable to protect the cap frame from the weather. The ogee Lincolnshire type has the breast beam almost completely exposed, as are the ends of the cap sheers which support it. No matter how well painted, these eventually decay, and the major job of replacement, sixty or more feet above the ground, has to be undertaken.

Sussex used a pepper-pot shape of cap on its tower mills, which protected the breast beam completely, as this was shorter and curved to the radius of the tower. The cap rafters, in many cases, rose up from a separate cap circle which was attached to the cap frame at suitable intervals. Nutbourne, Sussex, is a good example.

The Kentish cap undoubtedly protected the cap frame best of all, and had the added advantage of the vertical tail providing a lee which helped to protect the fantail timbers from the rain. Oddly enough, many North-western mills which used a primitive form of Kentish cap had the breast beam mounted outside in the rain, Weston, Shropshire and Willaston, Cheshire, being examples.

Wendover, Buckinghamshire. *An unusual octagonal tower mill of heavy build. A cast iron cross was used to attach the sails.*

Burgh-Le-Marsh, Lincolnshire. *Right: The five-sailed tower mill at work around 1962. The cap and fantail are typical of Lincolnshire.*

Stodmarsh, Kent. *A very rare small hollow post windpump. Once this was to be restored, but is now fast rotting away. Another example exists at the Singleton Open Air Museum in Sussex.*

COMPOSITE MILLS

A *composite mill* combined the principles of both post and tower mills, for the body of a post mill was mounted in the same way as a cap on a short tower. The post and trestle were removed. There seems to be no particular advantage in this arrangement except that there was more room for storage. Very few were built, and the last remaining example was at Little Laver in Essex. Readers should not confuse this with the arrangement found in Midlands post mills, where the body of the mill had a sub-frame with rollers attached below the spout floor. These rollers ran on a curb mounted on top of the roundhouse wall, and this curb took some weight and helped to steady the mill. The roundhouse roof turned with the mill as at Madingley (p.103). A variation was the use of a small curb built up from the quarterbars, the rollers in this case being attached to the sheer beams below the body, the long-gone mill at Bledlow Ridge, Buckinghamshire, being anexample.

The *sunk post mill* was another interesting variation, which dated back to the early days of windmills. Here the trestle was simply buried in a mound of earth, presumably to provide greater stability. The snags were that not only were the sails of necessity very short, but also the trestle could not be inspected for signs of the rot which would inevitably occur. There is no example of this type remaining in England.

The last oddity is the *hollow-post mill*. Here the brake wheel drove a slender upright shaft which passed right through the crowntree and down through a hole bored in the post. The upright shaft emerged beneath the crosstrees and drove the machinery in the roundhouse. The mill at Wimbledon Common, Surrey, was originally of this type, although the mill body is now mounted on a taller tower in the same way as a smock mill cap. The tiny pumping mill at Stodmarsh, Kent is a very good example of a hollow-post mill.

Marsh Mills

Windmills have been used for pumping for several centuries, and while a few like that at Faversham, Kent, were used for raising water from wells, their main use was for drainage.

Wind pumping mills were used in the years from the late seventeenth century onwards, becoming very popular indeed during the eighteenth and nineteenth centuries. Wind pumps were still being built in very limited numbers into the first years of the present century.

The most usual type found is the tower mill, although there were many smock mills in the past. The brake wheel drove the wallower on a very long upright shaft which terminated in a bevel gear on the ground floor. This gear drove a horizontal shaft which passed out of the mill and into a narrow semicircular casing positioned over a culvert outside the mill. Inside the casing was a large-diameter wheel with paddles attached around the rim. The paddles fitted the culvert closely, and when the wheel was rotated by wind power the water was swept up to a higher

Horsey, Norfolk. *A restored drainage mill with a stack of thatching reeds in the foreground.*

Stracey Arms, Norfolk.
An Appold turbine.

Upton. *A small pumping mill that once stood near Acle, Norfolk, now at Upton. There are spring sails and vane winding.*

level where it flowed into a canal. The scoop wheel could not lift water very far, but was simple in operation and was the mainstay of fen pumping for many years. Plunger pumps lifted further, but were mainly used in connection with wells, their use on marshes being rare.

The *Appold turbine* (Stracey Arms) was a more recent type of marsh pump, and worked in a cylindrical casing in the culvert. The vertical shaft carried a number of vanes which caused the water to rise up and flow out of the casing at a higher point. The principle is similar to that noticed when a cup of tea is stirred too fast.

Some very strange contraptions were used as wind pumps, not the least peculiar being the use of bare smock mill frames winded with tailpoles and carrying large common sails. Stodmarsh, Kent (p.38) typifies a very rare type of hollow post mill, and should be restored as this, and one from near Acle and now at Upton, Norfolk are two of the very last examples. Many dozens must have existed in the fens, and yet the Stodmarsh pump survives in a county where virtually no wind drainage mills existed.

Few complete drainage mills remain, and only Wicken Fen, Cambridgeshire, and Herringfleet, Suffolk, work occasionally, and then only for demonstration purposes. The rate of deterioration seems high, for, although most have the characteristic Norfolk-shaped cap which protects the timbers well from the elements, the majority remain as empty towers. A few mills were left high and dry by the receding water and were converted to corn mills. These must have worked well, for flat areas are good for wind.

Fortunately, the current surge in interest in windmills has been reflected in the restoration of drainage mills, and by the mid-1990s it was possible to see several marsh mills turning to wind, their owners intending to reinstate the sails and once again fill the flat lands around Acle with the quiet grace of turning sails.

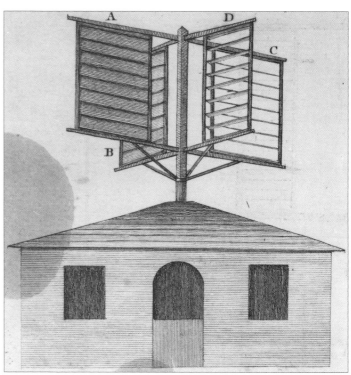

A horizontal mill. *A design by Robert Beatson in the 1790s. This type of mill is very inefficient, but eliminates the problems of turning to wind. The shutters blew open in one direction and locked in the other. There is no visible shutter control.*

HORIZONTAL MILLS

While on the subject of unusual windmills, it might be as well to say a few words about horizontal windmills, Examples have been built at both Margate and Battersea, both to the design of the same man. A tall tower was built in the manner of a lightly constructed smock mill tower. The machinery was contained in the lower floors, while the upper part had vertical louvres around the circumference. The wind blew through these and activated a large horizontal paddle-wheel, which was attached to an upright shaft. The louvres were inclined at an angle to enable the wind to impinge on only one side of the paddle-wheel no matter from which direction it was blowing. Nothing of these two mills remains. Robert Beatson, in his *Essay on the Comparative Advantages of Vertical and Horizontal Windmills* (1798), shows a horizontal windmill of his own invention. A shaft projects through the roof of a building and carries four blades. Each blade is constructed with shutters like a patent sail. The idea was that the wind would open the shutters from one side, but close those on the other. The difference in wind-resistance would cause the blades to rotate the shaft, and as each open blade came round the wind would close the shutters as it struck it from the opposite side. It would be most interesting to know whether any mills of this type were constructed.

Left: **Thornham Magna, Suffolk.** *Typical Suffolk breast framing. The surface is curved and the weather boarding sprung round. This mill last worked with two common and two patent sails, probably for reasons for saving weight.*

WINDMILL CONSTRUCTION

Apart from certain design features, old windmills have one characteristic in common – that of the use of large-section timbers, usually of oak. There was a timber in Keymer mill against which rested a rope. The movement of the body was such that the hundred years or more of abrasion had cut a groove so deeply into the oak that it was possible to insert a finger. The seasoned timber was known to be extremely hard and one day a man was in the roundhouse, speaking scathingly of the ancient structure. Mr Driver picked up a mallet and chisel and handed them to him. "If you can drive that chisel an inch into that post, I'll give you a shilling. If you can't, you give me a shilling; and if you break my chisel, you buy me another." The miller won his shilling.

A study of most old constructions, horse carriages for example, reveals that the timbers became of smaller and smaller section as time progressed. These were both strong and light when new, but as soon as a little weakness develops much rebuilding is required. Windmills seem to have undergone this change also, and a study of post mill corner posts will illustrate this well. Pitch pine is both strong and light, but rots more quickly than oak. Given the same degree of neglect, a pine mill will become weak years before its oak counterpart.

Smock mills were usually constructed piece by piece, with the cant posts being erected and the diagonal braces and floor beams fitted into their respective mortices, from the bottom upwards. A suggestion has been made that post mills were constructed piece by piece, with one side girt being put up at a time and the corner post fitted into its mortices on the upper and lower side girts while these were suspended in mid-air, no scaffolding being used. A millwright of the old school maintained that such a practice would be impossible, and that the only method of construction was that or raising complete sections of framing. The author used the latter method when constructing a one-third size post mill, as the other was quite unrealistic. The crowntree was tied down to the crosstrees at both ends, and first one side and then the other hoisted. An assistant fitted the cross members in the breast and tail as the second side was positioned.

For hoisting, the millwrights probably used a tall pole held upright by guy ropes. A strong block and tackle was suspended from the top; windshafts weighing many tons were raised by such devices. The main timbers were formed either by a hand saw and saw pit or, in older mills, by the use of an adze. The adze was a most useful tool consisting of a sharp blade with a handle about four feet long. A skilled man could use this axe-like tool with extreme accuracy.

It is probable that the millwrights followed the practice of most builders and carpenters and formed the basic timbers in their workshop. These would be brought to the mill site as required. The boards and minor timbers would be cut to size as the work proceeded.

Above: **Woolpit, Suffolk**. *The steeply cambered lower crosstree which enabled the piers to be of almost equal height. This feature is East Anglian in character, but a lower crosstree which is cambered at a lesser angle remains at Windmill Hill, Sussex.*

Lowfield Heath, Surrey. *Framing. This upright passes from a point just to the rear of the crowntree to the lower side girt. A very common arrangement in Sussex post mills.*

Left: **Windmill Hill, Sussex**. *A typical Sussex example of breast framing. The vertical boards were covered with an outer layer of horizontal weather boarding.*

Part Two
The Mechanism

Woolpit, Suffolk. *Fine workmanship. One of the wooden tram wheels.*

Chapter 4

The Sails

The earliest known sails were cloth-covered frames and probably had a constant *weather* (the inclination of the sail frame to the direction of the wind) all the way from the *heel* to the *tip*. Later *cloth* or *common* sails had many more sail bars to support the cloth when in use, and as the heel is going slowly but the tip relatively fast, the sail was given a greater angle at the heel and a much lesser one at the tip. This is very clear in the photograph of a common sail at Drinkstone, Suffolk. The same principle exactly is used on aircraft propellers. As can be seen in the photograph of Burgh-Le-Marsh mill (p.37) some millwrights favoured a sharper angle at the tip, whereas others, as at Drinkstone, favoured very little. The most usual measurement was something like 23 degrees with a maximum of 30 degrees at the heel, and about 3–5 degrees at the tip. The author once constructed some sails for a one-third size mill which were 30 degrees at the heel and zero degrees at the last sail bar. These sails were very powerful in use.

The cloth on these common sails could be furled like a curtain, and many had a type of curtail-rail at the heel to enable the cloth to be completely furled. Drinkstone and many others did not have this luxury, and a little cloth is kept on at all times. This does not matter as, since this is right at the heel, there is relatively little turning effect against the brake.

The *sail bars* are morticed through the *sail whip* and emerge on the leading side. The leading side often has a *leading board* which may extend part or all the way from heel to tip. The trailing or driving side has the tips of the sail bars connected by the *hemlath*. The *whip* is bolted and clamped to the *sail stock*, which extends for about half the sail length, and stays brace the inner sail bars from the *stock*.

The sequence on pages 48 and 49 show the erection of sails at High Salvington, Sussex. The stock is the most difficult to erect as it is very heavy, and has to be hoisted with the use of a block and tackle suspended from the poll end. The sails are hoisted in the same way and, being relatively light (four men can easily carry a small sail as shown here), present little difficulty. The greatest trouble comes when the sail has to be turned up to the top to enable the opposite sail to be fitted. Ropes are attached to the ends of the other sails, and, with much heaving, the sails are turned. E. Hole and Son use winches for this job, and this is most certainly the easiest and safest method. If ropes have not been properly attached to the odd sail, there is a real risk of it turning too far and running round out of control. This should be avoided at all costs, as it could well kill someone on its way round to the lowest position.

Before erecting sails it is important to ascertain that the mill is basically sound, for this work puts considerable strain on the breast beam, much of it from the side.

Common sails are very light and very powerful, but have the disadvantage of having to be stopped in order to furl the cloth. This cloth can be spread in several positions, varying from furled to full sail. The trouble was that if the mill was

Drinkstone, Suffolk. *A common cloth covered sail. The cloth is shown in the furled position.*

47

High Salvington, Sussex. *A sail about to be hoisted by E. Hole and Son.*

The sail being hoisted by a winch that is situated to the right of the photographer.

turning too fast and the miller wanted to furl the cloth a little, the mill had to be stopped with the brake. This could prove impossible if a sudden strong wind sprang up, the great danger being that the mill might run out of grain and the stones run dry. This could result in a shower of sparks which could well set the mill on fire. The other risk was that the speed of the sails might become so great that the mill might be shaken to pieces by the vibration. Placed in this position, the miller would try to ride out the storm, choking the stones with too much grain to slow them, or try to turn the sails edge on to the wind, the danger with the latter method being that a sudden slight change of wind could cause a tail-wind and blow the windshaft out of the mill. Another method of stopping the mill was to throw an abrasive, such as brick dust, on to the rim of the brake wheel. This method was used successfully by the late Mr D. Driver when the post mill he was working, at Keymer, Sussex, ran away on bare sail frames during a particularly high gale in 1912.

Mr Driver then worked for his uncle, a Mr White, and at the time was 18 years old. The post mill at Keymer still exists, although a total rebuild in progress at the time of writing will leave it with very few original timbers that the miller would recognise. The mill is old and low, with the trestle on short piers, allowing the spring sails (see below) to pass very close to the ground. The layout is head and tail with a later iron windshaft.

The gale came up from the south, the miller working "wind hours" and con-tinuing into the night. At seven o'clock in the evening Mr Driver opened the shutters fully, the gale continuing to rage and the mill running at full speed. The body was rolling and shaking so violently that, when Mr White came into the

Only a few feet to go. The man on the sail is ready to fit the first bolt.

mill at midnight, he pronounced that it was unsafe to continue and that the mill must be brought to a halt.

The grain being ground at the time was oats, which apparently leaves a dust that is more slippery than other grains. When the brake was lowered it refused to hold and the brick dust was used to bring the sails to a standstill. At the last moment Mr Driver leant out of the side window to position the sails accurately and a huge gust whisked his cap away into the blackness. It was returned the next day, having been picked up at Chimneys Hill, some three-quarters of a mile away!

A partial solution was patented in 1772 by the Scot, Andrew Meikle, this being a type of sail known as the *spring sail*. The spaces between the sail bars are larger, and in each bay two or three shutters are positioned. These shutters are hinged at either end and have a small crank fitted at one hinge. This crank is attached to the *shutter bar* which connects all the shutters of the sail together. If the sail is double shuttered as at Drinkstone (p.46) there are two rows of shutters, one on the leading side and one on the trailing side. The shutter bars are attached at the heel to a spring, the tension of which can be adjusted by a lever from the sail tip. The method of adjusting the spring tension varies from a simple lever to a rack and pinion, as at Ash and other Kentish mills. The springs vary also and may be full, or quarter elliptical, or even flat as at Drinkstone (p.50). The most usual is the full elliptical as at Outwood (p.50).

The wind presses against the shutters and tries to force them open against the spring. Thus it will be seen that the shutters partly open in a strong gust, allowing the wind to pass through. In heavy winds the miller only sets a light tension on the springs, the shutters being partly open most of the time.

The shutters are usually of wood, but have been made of metal in a few cases. A shuttered sail is heavy, and one method of reducing this weight was that of constructing a light wooden or metal frame for each shutter and covering this with thickly painted canvas. The shutters at Chillenden (p.21) have been of this type, but the canvas has been removed to reduce wind-resistance. The whole operation of a shuttered sail is very similar to that of a Venetian blind. Spring sails do have the disadvantage of having to be adjusted individually and the mill having to be stopped for each sail adjustment.

In 1807 Sir William Cubitt invented the *patent self-reefing sail*, which was the first type of sail to be reefed from within the mill. The construction of the patent sail was quite simple, for the shutter bars of the spring sail were connected

Drinkstone, Suffolk. *A spring sail with the shutters in the open position. The unusual control spring may be seen just above the inner sail bar.*

Outwood, Surrey. *Spring sails with the shutters in the closed position. The springs are of the more common design.*

together by the *spider*, which was positioned just forward of the poll end. The spider was connected to each shutter bar by cranks known as *triangles* and to the interior of the mill by the *striking rod* which passed right through the windshaft and emerged at the rear of the tail bearing. By pushing the striking rod in or out, the spider operates the triangles and so opens and closes the shutters.

Self-regulation was provided by two methods. The simplest is the *rocking lever* which protrudes from the rear of the cap on most Lincolnshire and Kentish mills. A chain hangs from the end of this lever and descends to the ground, and back up to the fantail where it passes over a pulley and down to the rocking lever. By pulling on one or other side of this chain, the rocking lever is hauled either up or down. When hauled up the lever opens the shutters, and a weight is hung on the chain to keep them open. Sometimes a catch is used to keep the rocking lever up. By hauling the rocking lever down, the shutters are closed against the wind-pressure. The wind tries to lift the lever, but by hanging various weights on the chain the miller can regulate the effort required to open the shutters and so the speed of the mill.

The other method is that usually found in post mills, and many Sussex tower and smock mills. This uses a rack attached to the end of the striking rod which may be moved in or out by rotating a shaft on which is mounted a pinion. The other end of this pinion shaft has a wheel (often the rim has a number of radial Y-shaped forks which give the chain a better grip), around the rim of which hangs an endless chain. By pulling on the chain the striking rod can be moved in or out; weights are hung on the chain to produce the same regulating effect found with the rocking lever. Many Norfolk tower mills use this method and have a pole which extends from the cap and steadies the chain where it hangs outside.

The chain is often operated from the top of the ladder of post mills and the wheel projects out of the tail. Many Sussex mills had the Y-wheel flat on the tail and operated the pinion shaft by means of a pair of bevel gears. Sometimes the

Windmill Hill, Sussex.
A very rare arrangement. The sweep governor which controlled the sail shutters via ordinary patent type mechanism.

North Leverton, Nottinghamshire.
Patent sails in use in a good breeze that is partially opening the shutters. The sails are mounted on a cross.

mechanism was fully enclosed within the mill as at Woolpit, Suffolk. Cross-in-Hand mill, Sussex, uses a short rocking lever with a box on the end in which the weights are placed (p.71). Windmill Hill, Sussex used a very rare device known as the *sweep governor*; this operated the shutters through the ordinary wheel-and-chain mechanism. The advantage of this complicated device is debatable, but its purpose was presumably to keep the mill running at an even speed. A set of patent sails with the shutters partly opened by the wind can be seen at North Leverton, Nottinghamshire. This mill has the sails fitted to a more recent device than the poll end. This is known as the *cross*, and is a large iron casting mounted on the end of the windshaft. Wendover, Buckinghamshire has a cross clearly displayed. The cross is almost universal in the North and North-east and, while usually used in conjunction with an iron windshaft, is fitted to a wooden shaft in the same way as a poll end. Stocks are not usually used with this type of sail fixing, and the whip is very much strengthened and called the *sail back*. The sail back is bolted directly to the cross. The poll end is almost universal in the South, although West Blatchington smock mill, Sussex, uses a cross with short stocks and ordinary whips mounted on them. East Blatchington tower mill also used a cross although this pumping mill was not a typical Sussex mill.

Some millers sought to obtain both power, from a pair of light common sails, and some self-regulation from a pair of spring sails, as at Drinkstone (p.50). Others used a pair of common sails together with a pair of patent sails as at Thornham Magna, Suffolk (p.42). Some patent sails had an air brake which consisted of a leading board which opened at right angles to the direction of rotation when the shutters opened. A type of sail which is very rare today, but which was often used in Yorkshire and the North, was the *roller reefing sail*, which had a number of roller blinds instead of shutters and was operated by a striking rod in the same way as the patent sail (Tollerton).

With the coming of patent sails which could be operated from within the mill, tower mills were built much higher, and many sails required very tall ladders to reach them, the Lincolnshire mills like Alford (p.119) being typical.

The use of the cross and sail back enabled mills to be built with more than four sails. These multi-sailed mills had five, six, eight, or in one case twelve sails and were most common in Lincolnshire. A five-sailed mill has the disadvantage of having to stop work if a sail becomes damaged, whereas a six-sailed mill is able to continue with four, three or two sails. Eight-sailed mills were not common, and are reputed to have suffered from the effects of turbulence caused by so many sails; one remains at Heckington, Lincolnshire.

Although a cross was usually used, a post mill with a three-way poll end stood at Ashcombe, near Lewes, Sussex. The late Mr D. Driver from Keymer post mill, Sussex, confirmed that as far as he could remember, the smock mill at South Common, Chailey (pulled down 1911), had six sails. He could not remember the type of sail fixing however. A very few annular sails have been used, but none now survives. One advantage of this type of sail and of multi-sailed mills is the smooth running produced. A post mill with four sails rolls and shakes to a surprising degree as each sail reaches the highest point and receives the full force of the wind. When two sails are in use many millers are fearful of running the mill at full speed, for the twisting effect is very noticeable even on smock mills.

Tollerton, Yorkshire. *In the 1930s. Roller reefing sails with blinds operated by the fork shaped bars that were controlled by patent type striking gear.* (Photograph: F.W. Gregory)

Sails have to be replaced at fairly frequent intervals. A good stock should last forty years and a good pair of sail frames fifty or even more. The stock takes a considerable strain and usually weakens at the poll end where water often lies. Bolt-holes can trap water too, and bolts should be avoided and clamps used where possible. When carrying out sail repairs it is an utterly false economy to settle for cheaper timber. A good pitch pine stock can cost a considerable amount today, but will last a very long time. Oak stocks are very long-lasting, but are also very heavy. An Oregon pine stock may be cheaper in the short term, but if it snaps and wrecks a good sail, or comes off backwards on to the mill roof, it can prove to be very expensive in the end. The post mill at Cross-in-Hand (p.189) has probably stopped for good due to a stock snapping in this manner.

The sails of four-sailed mills are usually left in the form of a St Andrew's Cross as this equalises the strain on the stocks. The greatest strain is suffered by a stock resting in a horizontal position.

Burwell, Cambridgeshire. *Patent sails showing the typical clockwise rotation and acute weather (26 to 16 degrees) of the area. Theoretically not a good design, but in practice these sails worked very well.*

The vertical position is the least straining. Mills like Stone Cross, Sussex, which operated with two sails up to ceasing work in about 1936, and whose miller always left them in the vertical position, often still retain the original sails to this day, in spite of having, as at Stone Cross, the extra resistance of a full set of shutters for some thirty years and being out of work for more than sixty years.

Mills which started life with common sails often have rather thin stocks (they are only about nine inches thick at High Salvington) and if, like Drinkstone, they have had a pair of heavier spring sails added, these are often left in the vertical position to reduce the strain on the stock (p.33).

Some old windshafts were bored from end to end in order to fit patent sails. This was done both on wood and iron shafts by setting up a drill at the tail bearing. The mill was then set to work while the drill was slowly fed in by the millwrights.

There is room for further recording of sails. The design varies from one area to another and the remaining examples of period working sails should be very carefully recorded. There is an area of east Cambridgeshire and north-west Suffolk

54

where double shuttered sails with 26 degrees weather at the heel and 16 degrees at the tip were used. This is vastly more weather than was used elsewhere at the tip, but the sails appear to have been very powerful and apparently started well (Burwell). The ability to start and run in a light wind is more useful than the attainment of high revolutions in a gale. In the words of Mr Chris Wilson of Over, whose windmill is fitted with these sails; "what you want is the grunt at the bottom end".

When I was a child there was an elderly schoolmaster living not far from the premises of E. Hole and Son. He had, he claimed, when a child, grabbed hold of the turning sails of Oldland post mill, Keymer and been taken round for a complete turn. How he held on, I cannot imagine, for the speed would have to be precisely right to hold him out radially without tearing his grasp from the sail bar. There has been much controversy over the issue of people going round on the sails, but in this case I received the tale first-hand.

A little further down the same road, there was once a post mill which was pulled down in 1914. An old retired carter could remember this mill at work and also a unique use found for the sails when the mill was disused: a boy with an intense loathing of school used to climb out onto the sails first thing in the morning and refuse to come down until after the scholastic day was over. Needless to say, no adult had the nerve to clamber out of the storm hatch and drag him down!

There is a great deal of tradition involved in sail design and it is possible to place a sail accurately to a given area after a careful study of its layout and proportions. The tradition is guided by practicality. For example, a wide shuttered sail with strong weather is of necessity normally double shuttered, for were it otherwise, the open shutters would foul the mill body. Two of the original sails at Upminster were made with a wider leading side than trailing for precisely this reason. Why there was a tradition of clockwise sails in Cambridgeshire and West Suffolk is not easily explained, other than that there was apparently an unusually large number of left-handed people in the area.

While multi-sailed mills have existed in most parts of the windmilling areas of the country, Lincolnshire is where they are most commonly met. At the present time it is possible to eat flour ground in four, five, six and eight-sailed Lincolnshire windmills. Those that have been restored to working order include Alford, Boston, Burgh-le-Marsh, Kirton-in-Lindsey, Heckington, Lincoln, Sibsey, Waltham and Wrawby. An impressive list!

In the past, sails would be left in the position that created the least strain; hence two sails would be vertical, four like a St Andrew's Cross, five with the lowest vertical (three at minimum strain), six with two horizontal (four at minimum strain) and eight with one pair vertical (six at minimum strain). There was clearly also an eye for neatness. A strange habit seems to have arisen recently whereby some six-sailed mills are left with one pair vertical and four sails at maximum strain. This not only strains more sails than necessary, but looks untidy.

It has long been assumed that eight sails was the greatest number fitted to English windmills, but a recently discovered photograph shows a tower mill at Cottenham, Cambridgeshire with no fewer than twelve narrow sails. This must have been very smooth in action, but I have to say that while a mill like Heckington is impressive by its sheer mass, I have a preference from an aesthetic point of view for windmills with four, and a maximum of six, sails.

Left: **Wingham, Kent.** *The neckbearing. The brass-lined iron bearing housing rests on the chair block which in turn is supported by the breast beam (out of sight). The storm hatch above gave access to the poll end and sails.*

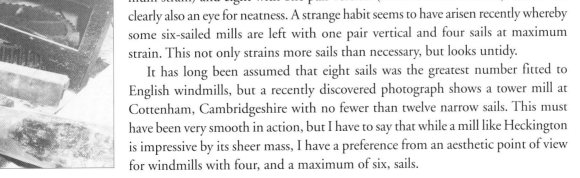

Left: **North Leverton, Nottinghamshire.** *The tail bearing. The support for the rocking lever and the striking rod are to the left. The gear cluster to provide the reduction for the fantail is to the rear.*

Chapter 5

The Fantail

The *fantail*, or *fly* as it is known in the eastern counties, is an ingenious device invented in the mid-1700s by Edmund Lee, its purpose being to keep the sails facing the wind at all times quite automatically. The simplest type is that seen below where the cap sheers are extended at the rear and a small fan-stage built. From the fan-stage two *fly posts* rise. These are braced to the cap, and the whole construction is very sturdy. At the top of each fly post is a bearing which supports the end of a spindle, known as the *fan* or *fly spindle*. In the centre of the spindle is a hub known as the *fan star* to which six or eight *fan stocks* are bolted. Each fan stock carries a fan blade.

The fan is connected by reduction gearing to a rack on the curb in the same way as the wheel-and-chain luffing gear. This gearing is very low and the fan may be revolved by using only finger pressure. A few turns of the fan will produce a barely discernable movement of the cap.

The fan is mounted at right angles to the sails, and while these face the wind, is edge on to the air flow. A slight change in the direction of the wind will strike the fan from the side, thereby causing it to rotate until the cap has once again been turned to face squarely into the wind and the fan is becalmed.

Most of the Lincolnshire type mills have an arrangement where the bevel gear on the fan spindle drives a long diagonal shaft which passes into the cap and operates a cluster of reduction gears inside, the final drive to the rack being via a

Sylenham, Suffolk. *The classic Suffolk fly, photographed in 1958.*

Stracey Arms, Norfolk. *A typical Norfolk cap and fantail. The wheel with the Y-shaped forks operates the striking gear via a rack and pinion.*

Cross-in-Hand, Sussex. *The tailpole fantail being refitted to a new tailplate after the mill had been struck by lightning. A pair of new sail frames and a stock are in the foreground.*

pinion. The mills of the south use a different approach, for the greater part of the reduction is usually created by several pairs of gears out on the fan stage. When the drive eventually enters the cap it is most commonly taken to the rack by means of a large worm. Some Kentish mills, like Sandwich and Charing, have enormous wooden worms which mesh with a rack of coarse wooden teeth with a pitch of about three inches.

Fan stages vary greatly in design from one area to another, those of Kent (p.100) being small and high, while those of the adjacent county, Sussex, are huge and spacious, the fans often having only five blades, as may still be seen at Polegate. The Lincolnshire fantails are the most alarming, for there is hardly any fan stage and when the miller wishes to lubricate the fan bearings, he is obliged to climb up a series of wooden blocks screwed to the high, sloping fly posts. A hand rail is provided, but the ground seems a very long way below. Sometimes a mill is equipped with a narrow gallery which extends from the fan stage round the side of the cap to the sails. This greatly eases the painting of the cap, which can be carried out safely without the use of a cradle.

A safety device which is fitted to most mills is the provision whereby the fan can be disconnected and a hand crank used to turn the mill in the event of the fan becoming damaged. The most common method of disengaging the fan is the use of a square sleeve to connect the two halves of one of the main shafts. The miller simply removes a small bolt and slides the sleeve out of engagement. Many Kentish mills had a Y-wheel and rope mounted on the side of the cap, the sole purpose of which was to provide emergency hand turning.

Should the wind suddenly change through 180 degrees in a thunderstorm, and strike the mill exactly from behind, the fan will not turn. The miller must then quickly crank the cap round a few degrees before reconnecting the fan, which will then turn the cap to face the wind. Failure to do this could result in a tailwind. Fantails are normally completely reliable and will always keep the sails facing the wind.

Post mills are often fitted with fantails, this being almost universal in Suffolk. The simplest method is that seen on p.6 where the fantail is mounted on the tailpole, and the fan drives the two wheels through reduction gearing. As the wheels slowly revolve they move the fan carriage round a level track, thus turning the mill. The ladder has a pair of wheels at its foot. The wheels of the ladder at Cross-in-Hand run on an iron track. The tailpole has to be very strong with this type of fantail, and before that at Cross-in-Hand was renewed it whipped so much that the ladder wheels could be seen moving backwards and forwards while the mill was at work. In spite of adequate lubrication of the pintle, the mill also tended to jerk round with loud cracks as the fantail flexed the tailpole before moving the mill. After replacement, the mill seemed far steadier while running, and the movement of the ladder wheels was greatly reduced. Only two original examples of this type of fantail remain: that of Cross-in-Hand, and the rebuilt one of Argos Hill nearby. Some Norfolk post mills used these fantails, but they were traditional in Sussex.

The *ladder fantail* (p.60) was used in Suffolk a great deal. This arrangement spread both north and south of Suffolk, but is believed not to have occurred south of the Thames. The author has, however, seen an engraving of a Sussex post mill where the fan looked suspiciously as if it was mounted on the ladder. An engraving cannot be relied upon as proof as it is not necessarily of great accuracy, although this one was so in other respects.

Ladder fantails usually have the fly posts inclined outwards at the top in order to allow the fan to catch the greatest wind without interference from the mill body, and also to push inwards at the foot. A little sideways skidding can occur if the mill rocks much on its post, and this outward leaning helps to counteract this and also relieve the body of the mill of some weight by counterbalancing the ladder. The drive to the tram wheels is the same as with a tailpole fantail. Some ladder fantails were very tall as at Friston (p.60), where the height can be judged by the man walking under the breast of the mill. The drive was usually taken by both tram wheels, but at Woolpit, Suffolk, the ladder fantail drove to only one wheel. The track at Woolpit was of large stones whereas some, like Syleham, were of gravel. Others were simply of large wooden slabs let into the ground.

The ladder had to be very strong when a ladder fantail was used, and to aid this much bracing was employed. Many mills had the fantail added at a later date, in which case the tailpole was usually cut off at the ladder, where it continued to take the lateral strain. Sometimes the tailpole continued through the slot in the ladder, and was attached to a crosspiece between the fly posts.

A more unusual type of post mill fantail was the *roof-mounted fantail*. This is found over a wide area and has been known in many of the more advanced windmilling counties. A fantail of this type remains at Icklesham, Sussex, and the remains of another were to be seen nearby at Winchelsea. The fan drives a train of reduction gears in the normal way, the drive passing right down the tail of the mill, down the ladder and driving the tram wheels at the foot. The drive has also been known to pass inside the mill and turn the body by means of a worm and rack on the post. The fan could be smaller with this type of fantail, as it was more exposed to the wind than the other types.

The fan usually spends its time making only a few turns either way, and even when the wind changes it does not run continually, but tends to run in short bursts, the mill following the wind round until it settles in the new position. The behaviour of the fan in a gale is rather more dramatic, and it frequently careers round first one way and then the other. Many millers will mention this, and Mr Dallaway from the smock mill at Punnetts Town, Sussex, remembers the fan vibrating the whole cap during the gales. This was later made worse by the replacement of a broken fan blade with a modified post mill blade. This was heavier than the others, resulting in a very out-of-balance fan which used to rock the whole fan stage up and down when running fast.

The fantail is a most fascinating part of a windmill, and it is an interesting exercise to compare the construction of those that remain. Fortunately a number are still in use and continue to turn mills – both working and disused. Frequent greasing is very necessary, failure to do this resulting in unnecessary strain and wear. A dead curb will soon seize up if left ungreased, although the fan may still turn the cap to face the strongest gales for a few more months. Even when greased, dead curbs tend to be stiff, and the cap moves round with loud creaks. To experience a gale in a smock mill with a dead curb is quite interesting, for, with the wind roaring in the sails, beating on the cap and vibrating the tower, the fan flies round, moving the cap with great cracking noises which can be heard throughout the mill. On such days only the bravest of enthusiasts ventures onto the fan stage.

In light winds the fan stage or cap gallery can be a most charming place, for while the fan may be felt turning the cap and the sails cause a little movement, the sensation is in no way alarming. To stand on the fan stage fifty or sixty feet above the ground watching the great white sails turning against the evening countryside is an entertainment no reader who has the chance should miss.

Icklesham, Sussex. *The faintail mounted on the roof. The drive passes down the tail of the mill to tram wheels at the foot of the ladder.*

Friston, Suffolk. *The most sophisticated post mill remaining in the world, shortly before ceasing work. The size should be compared with the man walking under the breast. This mill is currently being slowly restored to a highly authentic standard.*

CHAPTER 6

The Stones

A factor common to all corn windmills is the use of millstones for grinding the grain into flour. The mechanism of these will now be discussed.

The reader may remember that the top floor of a later post mill houses the bins for storing grain prior to grinding. Earlier post mills had two pairs of stones, one in the breast and the other in the tail, these being driven from above by the stone nut, which meshes with the brake or tail wheel.

From the bin above, a chute, which may be of wood or a simple cloth sleeve, feeds grain into the *hopper* which is mounted just above the stones on the stone-floor. Originally these hoppers were larger and no bin-floor was used. The miller had to keep filling them with grain continually as they only held about two sacks, and the introduction of a bin-floor with larger bins holding ten sacks or so was a great relief. Most of the remaining post mills have bins, either as the original concept or as an addition where they are crammed into the roof space with barely room to empty the sacks.

From the hopper, the grain flows through an opening controlled by a small slide and on to an inclined wooden trough called the *shoe*. The shoe and hopper are mounted in a frame known as the *horse* which is itself attached to the wooden

Burgh-Le-Marsh, Lincolnshire. *The stones and the horse with hopper and shoe. The wooden spring that holds the shoe into engagement with the quant is visible on the front of the stone vat. The stones are running.*

Drinkstone, Suffolk. *The tail stones. An unusual arrangement of hopper and horse where an oversize shoe is supported by the mill wall. The action of the quant (lower left) can be seen.*

Keymer, Sussex. *The stones with the vat removed. The brake wheel, stone nut and quant that drive the runner stone.*

stone casing called the *vat* or *tun*. The angle of the shoe can be controlled by a cord which passes over a pulley and down to a knob known as the *twist peg* on the spout-floor below. By operating the twist peg the miller can control the rate of flow of grain to the stones. The shoe is vibrated by a square on the *quant*, which is the vertical spindle carrying the stone nut. This vibration causes the grain to flow down the shoe and into the stones. The illustration on p.62 shows this very well, although that on p.63 is the more usual type with a small shoe, and the horse mounted entirely on the stone vat. An arrangement known as the *bell alarm* is often found, whereby a small bell rings if the hopper becomes empty. The most common way of operating this bell is that of having a wide leather strap nailed inside the hopper. A string is attached from the free end to a small bell which is suspended over a piece of moving machinery. The weight of the grain normally holds the strap firmly in the bottom of the hopper, but if this runs out the weight of the bell raises the strap which in turn allows the bell to touch the machinery. The ringing warns the miller, who either stops the mill or quickly takes some grain up to the bins before the stones run dry.

While most windmill historians would regard the bell alarm as an essential part of the mill, it is interesting to note that Mr Driver told me that one of his first acts when going to work at Keymer mill in the early years of this century, was to fit up a bell alarm. Presumably this mill had worked for virtually its entire life without this amenity.

There are two millstones, one stationary and imbedded in the floor, and the other *runner stone* which revolves above it. The runner stone has a round hole in the centre known as the *eye*. The grain pours from the shoe down through the eye, and is ground as it passes between the surfaces of the stones. Flour emerges at the outer edge where it is swept round inside the vat by a small paddle until it drops down a spout to the floor below.

In England, two basic types of stone are found – the *peak*, which is a one-piece stone mined in the Peak District, and the *French burr*, which is built up from a number of wedge-shaped pieces of hard quartz. Peak stones are rather coarse in texture and are used for cattle-food. The French burr is smooth and very hard and was used for flour production. The wedge-shaped pieces of stone were arranged in a special manner, and were both cemented and clamped together with iron bands around the circumference. The non-working surface was usually faced with plaster of Paris. Another imported stone, which is rarely found today, is the *Blue* or *Cullen stone*. This was a one-piece stone, with a rather smoother texture than the peak, which was imported from Germany. A stone often found in the North-west was the *red stone*, which had a texture like very hard sandstone. This was also a one-piece stone, mined locally. A pair of these stones may be seen at Gayton, Cheshire (p.35), where the tower appears to be built of the same type of stone.

DRESSING THE STONES

The grinding surface of the stones has a number of tangential grooves cut in it which convey the flour to the periphery. On each *land* between the furrows are cut a good number of fine grooves which actually carry out the grinding. The surface of the stone gradually wears, and the runner stone has to be lifted up for dressing. This is done by removing the vat and either winding a rope around the windshaft (where deep grooves are often worn) and using wind power, or using a block and tackle. This latter method has to be used in tower and smock mills due to the windshaft being out of reach. The stone is carefully laid on its back ready for the miller, or in the past the stone-dresser, to commence the skilled job of stone-dressing.

The furrows are deepened and the *stitching*, as the fine dressing is called, re-cut by means of a small handle which holds a very hard chisel-shaped *mill bill*. When grinding cattle-feed the *thrift*, as the handle is called, sometimes holds a pointed mill bill called a *pick*. This chips out small indentations in the lands. The surface must be level, and this is tested by drawing a wooden staff across the surface. The face of the staff is coated with red oxide which leaves a red mark on the high spots. The miller then chips these high spots away with the mill bill or rubs minor ones down with an old piece of burr stone, called the rubbing

Willesborough, Kent. *Dressing tools laid out on a peak bed stone. Two types of thrift may be seen, together with a couple each of bills and picks, a jack staff in place on the stone spindle, a wedge for holding the runner during raising, a staff standing at an angle against a sack barrow and a crow bar to insert between the stones to lever one edge of the runner up prior to raising.*

Moulton, Lincolnshire. *Thrifts, bills, picks and a small brush last used to dress the engine-driven stones in the early 1950s.*

Broadhill Mill, Sussex.
A pair of stones in the workshop with the runner lifted to show how the grain is broken down from the eye to emerge as flour at the skirt. Note the mace in position on the stone spindle.

A French burr stone.
The stone is dressed for flour milling. Note the fine stitching on the lands between the furrows.

burr. The runner stone must be slightly concave towards the eye to encourage all the grain to enter the gap. A small *eye staff* is used to test the level of the concave area. The staffs are tested occasionally against a proof staff which is very carefully preserved. One at Meopham, Kent, was of slate, although others were of iron. Any high spots or signs of warping on the staff were remedied with great precision. The dressing tools may be seen on p.65. The stitching is done after the stone has been levelled.

In the past, the first act of the stone dresser was to take off any obvious high spots or wear rings on the stone with a mill bill. The surface was then rubbed with the rubbing burr to remove sharp pieces that might scratch the staff and the stone was staffed. The high spots were then taken down with the bill until there was even marking over the surface. At this point a pick (a pointed version of the mill bill) was inserted in the thrift and the furrows were deepened. The latest variation of this process is the use of an angle grinder, which is a modern electrically driven cutting disk, to cut the sharp line of the furrows. This saves much work and time, the remainder of the furrow being formed with the pick and bill.

Stitching used to be placed on the lands between the furrows, but now the rough texture of a peak stone is often regarded as sufficient. A couple of retired millers who used peak stones driven by an engine have recently told me that they also used not to insert stitching. These same millers also stated that they did not give either bed or runner stone swallow (the slight dishing around the inner third of the face). There is obviously room for research in this area, for Mr Wilson of Over says he gives both stones swallow, whereas Mr Waterfield gives swallow only to the runner stone. Mr Waterfield's method is regarded as usual.

With regular use, a pair of flour stones used to be dressed every month. The modern miller allows his stones to run much longer, but then the standard required of the flour is not so high. It will be interesting to see whether the frequency of dressing increases if there is a movement towards flour that has been passed through a dresser.

In the garden of Mr Biggadike, the last miller of Moulton, there is a peak stone with very deeply cut furrows. Mr Biggadike thinks that this must have been dressed by an employee who dressed the stones too deeply, thus allowing whole grains to pass through and into the finished meal. There is a similarly dressed stone at Penny Hill, so maybe the employee worked there or there is some other purpose for this dressing.

There is a common misunderstanding where stones are concerned. The action of the furrows is not one of the sharp vertical edges crossing one another like scissors, it is the sloping, opposite side of the furrow that breaks open the grain and the fine stitching or cracking that carries out the fine grinding. A clockwise stone rotates in that direction when viewed from above. To ascertain the direction of rotation of a discarded millstone, place the hand against the face and move it in the direction of the sloping side of the furrows. This is the rotation of the stone.

There is scope for the careful recording of the dressing on old millstones, for there seems to be some variation in techniques used and certainly modern dressing is far less frequent. Unless one has dressed a millstone, there could well be some lack of awareness of what the last stone dresser has achieved. Enough to say that I have measured stitching on a flour stone that had been unused for one hundred years and found it to be at the legendary one-sixteenth of an inch apart. To dress that finely one needs a great deal of skill!

DRIVING THE STONES AND TENTERING

The runner stone is supported from below by the *stone spindle* which passes up through a bearing in the bed stone. The stone spindle must be vertical or the runner stone will not run true, and to test this a wood or iron bar, called the *jack staff*, fits to the upper end which projects above the bed stone. A feather is fitted to the end of the jack staff and, with an assistant turning the spindle from beneath, the miller is able to observe whether or not this touches the bed stone equally all the way round. If it does not then the bearing at the foot is adjusted by wedges or screws until the spindle is vertical.

A leather washer prevents dust entering the bearing in the bed stone. Above the washer the stone spindle rises as a tapering square, and the *mace* fits on to the square in such a way that the end of the spindle projects through with a rounded tip. The runner stone has a bar attached across the eye which has a recess in the centre, and the recess rests on the *cock head* (the rounded tip) of the stone spindle. The *bridge* in the eye of the runner stone engages with two recesses in the mace. Thus the runner stone is balanced on the cock head, but turns with the stone spindle.

The quant which carries the stone nut has a large fork formed in the end which engages with two more recesses in the mace. The upper end fits into a bearing in a *sprattle beam* just to the rear of the brake wheel. There is some slackness in the fitting of the quant at the mace, which enables the sprattle bearing to be released and the stone nut moved out of engagement with the brake wheel. This allows either pair of stones to be used as the miller wishes.

Later post mills often had two pairs of stones side by side in the breast, in which case the drive was through a wallower, upright shaft and great spur wheel (Saxtead Green, p.68). This was much favoured in Suffolk where a third pair was

Woolpit, Suffolk.
The sprattle beam that supports the upper bearing of the quant usually passes from side to side of the mill, but this rare one projects forward from the tail beam.

Winchelsea, Sussex.
A pair of cullen stones on the bin floor to the rear of the tail wheel which were said to be used for grinding beans. The drive was not clear, but said to be by belt.

sometimes driven in the usual way from the tailwheel. Some large post mills had four pairs of stones, with two pairs driven by both the brake and tail wheels.

The stone spindle rests in a footstep bearing which is situated on the *bridge tree* in the ceiling of the spout floor. The bridge tree is pivoted at one end and is supported at the other by a lever known as the *brayer*. The free end of the brayer is supported by the end of a long iron lever called the *steelyard*. The steelyard passes over a fulcrum and, being of considerable length, has very great leverage. A movement of one inch at the steelyard end produces nearly imperceptible movement of the stone spindle in a vertical direction. The miller can adjust the gap between the stones by means of a screw at the junction of the steelyard and the brayer. After starting the mill, the miller stands here feeling the flour as it emerges from the spout with his left hand, which is said to be more sensitive, and adjusting the screw with the other until the best setting is achieved.

In early days the miller had to continue adjusting the stones all day, for as the speed increases the runner stone tends to rise a few thousandths of an inch. Small as this measurement is, it is none the less able to alter the quality of flour, and the miller had to lower the stones a fraction. A gusty wind would require the miller to alter the adjustment almost incessantly. To avoid this trouble, a *governor* (below)

Saxtead Green, Suffolk. *The usual arrangement for driving two pairs of stones side by side in the breast.*

Shipley, Sussex. *The governors which control the gap between the stones. This late mill uses one pair to control all the stones.*

Silver Hill, Sussex. *The iron bridge tree, stone spindle and bridging box supported by an iron brayer with adjusting crank. A wooden device connects to the steelyard to move with it and move the twist peg (to the left) to reduce the feed to the shoe when the speed rises. This is an uncommon arrangement to try to even out the supply.*

was installed. This was usually belt-driven from the stone spindle, and as the speed of the mill increased the weights flew out causing a collar on the spindle to rise. A fork on the end of the steelyard engaged with this collar, and rose and fell as the speed changed. As the brayer and bridge tree were connected to the other end of the steelyard, it will be seen that the stone spindle also rose and fell quite automatically.

Many late windmills drove the stones from below – a method known as *under-drift* or *underdriven*. The arrangement was less common in post mills than in smock and tower mills, but there is such an example at Cross-in-Hand, Sussex. The only difference was that the stone nut was mounted on a square on the stone spindle and was raised out of engagement with the great spur wheel by means of a ring which pushed the stone nut up the spindle and out of mesh. The screw operation of this can be seen together with an iron bridge tree. In place of the quant a small iron forging called the *damsel* was used to vibrate the shoe. This can just be seen projecting above the right-hand stone vat in the photograph of Stanton opposite. The damsel was so called because, with its three or four arms striking the shoe, it made more noise than any other part of the windmill's mechanism. Political correctness obviously did not exist in the days of the windmill!

An odd arrangement found in some Midlands post mills is the *hurst*. The hurst is a stout framework which supports two pairs of stones, underdrift, side by side in the breast on the spout floor. The bed stone is only about four feet above the floor, and there is some difficulty in providing room for a reasonably large bin to receive the flour. The whole mechanism is very cramped and it is hard to see the advantage, if any, over other types of stone situation.

Cross-in-Hand, Sussex. Right: *A morticed iron great spur wheel driving a pair of stones underdrift in the breast. A cast iron bridge tree with screw for raising the stone nut from mesh is shown to the right.*

70

Stanton, Suffolk. *Two pairs of stones underdriven in the breast with a wooden upright shaft. At one time this mill drove a third pair of stones via a shaft from the brake wheel.*

North Leverton, Nottinghamshire. *Barley meal pouring into a sack.*

CHAPTER 7

—

Other Machinery

SACK HOISTS

To raise the grain to the bin floor the miler used the *sack hoist*. The simplest form of post mill sack hoist was that with a long roller mounted in the peak of the roof on the bin floor. A pulley was mounted on one end round which a slack belt or chain passed. The belt also passed round a pulley on the windshaft and, by using a jockey pulley or a system of levers which raised the pulley end of the sack hoist roller, the belt was tightened, thus revolving the roller. The other end of the roller had a chain attached which passed right down through the mill to the ground. When the hoist was used the miller usually tipped the sacks on the bin floor while the mill boy slipped a noose at the end of the chain round the neck of the sack. The control rope passed down to the ground too, and a jerk would signify that the sack was ready. The miller then operated the control cord, and the sack came up through a series of trap-doors so designed that the double flaps of which they were comprised fell shut behind it.

At the bin floor the sack could be balanced on the edge of the bin by slipping the drive, and provision is always made for this. The chain was then dropped to the ground through a good-sized hole at the joint of the two halves of the trap-doors. Tall post mills suffered from the difficulty of not being able to raise sacks from the bottom floor of a multi-floored roundhouse unless the mill faced in certain directions. The roundhouse roof does not meet the post, but joins a ring which is supported from the quarterbars at about a four-foot radius from the post. Sacks can, therefore, always be raised from a single-storey roundhouse, although often having a bumpy ride past the quarterbars on their way up.

An unusual type of sack hoist comprised an endless chain running from the dust floor to the ground floor in a tower mill, upon which short lengths of chain with a loop to form a running noose were attached, and which operated without the necessity of returning the empty chain to the ground.

Sack hoist drives are many and various, but even if the power take-off is through a gear, there is a friction arrangement in the system somewhere which allows the drive to be engaged without stopping the sails. Smock mills and tower mills also use very many forms of sack hoist drive, the most usual being the mounting of the sack hoist roller on the dust floor with a drum on the end engaging with a friction surface on the lower face of the wallower.

These drums varied from about eighteen inches in diameter to nearly four feet, as at Hildenborough. The sack hoist drive at Silver Hill mill, Hastings, was gear-driven from just above the great spur wheel, with the drive passing upwards via a leather belt. The sack traps were usually all in perfect line right up the mill and could be heard banging shut as the sacks passed through five or more floors. Some rather small mills had a hinged ladder to the bin floor, which could be moved to the vertical position and the aperture used to raise sacks, normal sack traps being used for the floors below.

Friston, Suffolk *when still at work. The brake wheel with two rows of teeth and the sack hoist bollard and drive in the roof overhead.*

Above: **Capenhurst, Cheshire.** *The wire machine. The spindle and the ends of the brushes can be seen in the end of the cylinder.*

Above right: **Argos Hill, Sussex.** *The grain cleaner with fan below to discharge the dust.*

Right: **Bexhill, Sussex.** *A jog scry or jumper used to grade the tailings from the wire machine.*

Shipley, Sussex.
A smutter.

BOLTERS AND WIRE MACHINES

When the flour emerges from the stones it is quite warm and is allowed to cool in wooden bins on the spout floor. The miller then bags it up and hoists it to the bin floor, where he empties the sacks into another bin. This bin originally fed the *bolter* which consisted of an inclined cylindical wooden frame covered by a woollen sleeve. The mesh of this sleeve was fine at the top and became coarse towards the bottom. The cylinder was rotated by a pulley attached to a shaft running through the centre.

The coarse flour was fed in at the top end by a shoe similar to that used at the stones. As the cylinder revolved the finest flour passed through the first mesh and was collected in a chute. The coarser flour was collected in the next, and the very coarse flour in the next, while the bran tailed out of the end. To encourage the passage of the flour through the cloth, a number of springy wooden bars were positioned to rap against the cylinder frame, which was thus vibrated. A bolter is rarely found in a windmill today, although the barest remains of one were to be seen at Shiremark, Surrey.

The bolter was superseded by the *wire machine*, which, although operating on the same principle, differed in that there was a fixed cylinder covered with various meshes of wire. The spindle drove four brushes or more, which revolved inside the cylinder and brushed the flour through as the meal descended from the shoe. A wire machine with the access covers removed may be seen in the picture of Capenhurst. The various grades of flour emerge on the floor below, from chutes which feed directly into sacks.

The *jog scry* was an older form of flour dresser, which consisted of an inclined chute with several grades of mesh forming a false floor. One end was hinged while the other was jerked up and down by a long belt attached either to a short throw crank or to a lever which was moved up and down by a number of cams, looking similar to a very coarse gear wheel. That shown in the photograph of Bexhill was used to grade the bran as it emerged from the wire machine.

Mr Wright of Friston mill tells me that when the jog scry was in use the sound of sixteen teeth striking the cam at fifteen revolutions per minute could be heard over the entire village!

Other machines found were *smutters* (Shipley), which attempted to remove the black fungus which sometimes attacks wheat, and *grain cleaners* (Argos Hill) which often did not have the fan, seen here, for blowing away the dust. Both use the same principle as the wire machine. Argos Hill mill, shown here also had a

Bardwell, Suffolk.
Auxiliary drive from the upright shaft via wooden bevel gears.

Clayton Post Mill, Sussex. *Auxiliary drive with cross shaft below the windshaft, necessitating a skew gear.*

wind-driven grindstone, which would have been used to sharpen the miller's mill bills.

The problem of space was not great with smock and tower mills, where such machines were easily fitted in. Post mills usually had an extension (High Salvington, p.133) to the rear of the corner posts in which these machines could be housed. Argos Hill mill has an extension upon the extension, this reaching only about two-thirds of the way up. Bolters and wire machines were nearly always mounted crossways in the tail of post mills and were rather shorter than that shown at Capenhurst. The drive to bolters and wire machines varied greatly but was usually taken from a bevel ring on the great spur wheel, or from a separate bevel gear (above) mounted on the upright shaft in tower and smock mills. Post mills often had a skew gear mounted on a crossways shaft and driven from the brake wheel, the drive then being by a long belt to a pulley in the tail.

The photograph below shows a nice wooden skew gear at Clayton post mill.

GEAR TYPES AND VARIATIONS

Some of the greatest skill was required by the millwrights when making the wooden gears. These had to be very strong and yet perfectly round, with the teeth spaced at the correct pitch. The earliest type of brake wheel was that known as the *compass arm* type, where two spokes were morticed right through the windshaft in the form of a cross. To the ends of these spokes four or six *cants* were fitted which formed the rim. The ends were joined with tenons and bolts, while more curved pieces of timber formed a ring which crossed the joints on either face.

A large number of wooden pegs were mortised right through the rim and emerged on the far face, where they were pinned. These pegs engaged with a stone nut of the lantern pinion type. This consisted of two solid wooden discs joined by a number of staves. The result was similar to a cylindrical bird-cage or an old-fashioned lantern. The quant passed through a square hole in the centre of each of the wooden discs.

The *trundle wheel* was a development of the lantern pinion in which the top disc was removed leaving the staves projecting upwards. These engaged with the brake wheel pegs in the same way as the lantern pinion.

The later wheels had proper wooden teeth around the rim which engaged with an early type of wooden bevel gear. This type of stone nut was bound with iron and appeared very similar to a wooden cart hub (below).

The first brake wheels were face gears where there was no bevel, the teeth being entirely square to the radius. The wallower, of course, was normally a shallow bevel gear to suit the inclination of the windshaft.

Lowfield Heath, Surrey. *The auxiliary take off with short shaft on the radius of the brake wheel.*

Rolvenden, Kent. *A wooden stone nut engaging with the brake wheel.*

The principle of the bevel gear is one where the driving faces of the two gears are bevelled at such an angle that if they were cones, their tips would meet at the theoretical point of contact of the centres of the two shafts. The bisecting of the angle of the two gears in this way ensures an even contact between the faces of the teeth. While the theory was clearly known and used by the millwrights for such items as fantail gears, many brake wheels were built as face gears. Rolvenden and Wingham being examples from Kent. In order to secure even loading throughout their contact, the teeth of face gears were frequently trimmed to unusual shapes as seen at Wingham. Where direct drive to the stones is employed as in a head and tail post mill, the difference in size between the two gears is so great that the optimum angle of bevel is quite shallow. This, coupled with the fact that the brake wheel teeth comprise only a small part of the radius, probably led some millwrights to disregard the optimum sophistication of the bevel gear. In a tower mill like Wingham, the wallower is relatively large and with a more acute angle required, the problems of obtaining a decent mesh far greater.

The compass arm wheels were not as easy to keep true as some later types, and surprisingly few remain to this day. Many wallowers were compass-arm, and often had the upper and lower surfaces covered in with thick planks, the result looking

Ash, Kent. *A fine wooden stone nut trapped amongst the remains of the collapsed post mill.*

Windmill Hill, Sussex. *The morticed iron tailwheel with large mortices necessitating stepped teeth to accommodate the stone nut teeth.*

like a solid wheel. A pair of compass arm wheels meshing together is very rare, although a compass arm brake wheel and wallower may be seen at Weston, Shropshire. Wallower rims were frequently laminated to reduce the possibility of splitting.

Most wooden brake and tail wheels are of the *clasp arm* type where the timbers form a square through which the windshaft fits (Clayton). Many later windshafts had a square formed at each wheel position for this purpose. A good number of mills have had compass arm wheels converted to clasp arm, as has the wheel at Clayton. It is interesting to compare the heavy construction of Clayton with the lighter construction of Winchelsea (p.80). The latter is probably the younger.

Great spur wheels were also of compass or clasp arm construction. Most compass arm wheels had four spokes (p.80), but some had six, as at Nonnington, Kent, and others had eight, as at Hildenborough in the same county (p.81). The four intermediate spokes on this last did not pass right through and only entered the upright shaft for a depth of about four inches. Compass arm great spur wheels were not uncommon in Kent, although most had four arms, more than this number presumably causing a weakness of the upright shaft.

Clasp arm great spur wheels are often seen, a very fine example being at Chislet (p.81), where the entire weight of the upright shaft and stones was taken by a very substantial hurst frame. This method is rare, and it would be quite possible to dismantle the entire tower, but still leave the stones and upright shaft standing.

By far the most common constructional material to be found in windmill gears today is iron. Many old wooden gears have been replaced by cast iron, and some have had the teeth cut off and iron teeth bolted on in sections (p.62). Most of the remaining stone nuts are of cast iron. Cast-iron gears last almost indefinitely but, if meshing with another iron-toothed gear, can be extremely noisy.

Wingham, Kent. *Details of the brake wheel which was a face gear with unusually shaped teeth to ensure suitable meshing with the iron wallower.*

Below right: **Whitstable, Kent.** *The four armed great spur wheel of compass arm design.*

Below: **Winchelsea, Sussex.** *A clasp arm brake wheel of refined design. The windshaft had long been missing. This and the matching tail wheel are feared to have been lost during past repair.*

Nonnington, Kent. *A six armed compass great spur spurr wheel. Wheels of this design with four or six arms were not unusual in Kent.*

Pakenham Mill, Suffolk, used to have a small pair of stones driven by an iron stone nut from an iron internal ring on the great spur wheel (p.34). The noise was most striking and was made far worse by the ring being out of true. A local millwright blamed this on the wooden pattern warping before being used the make the mould.

To reduce the noise many millwrights fitted wooden teeth to iron wheels; these were known as morticed iron wheels (p.82). Wood to wood, or wood to iron is an almost silent drive, and only the faintest purring is audible. Wooden teeth were usually made of apple wood, although other tough, hard woods like Holly and hornbeam were also used. These teeth do not wear very much, and if well lubricated with grease or linseed oil, will last half a lifetime.

The shanks of the teeth usually projected through the rim and were held with two small nails driven in towards each other (p.79). An older method was that of driving wedges between the shanks as at Friston (p.82).

A very rare arrangement may be seen at Madingley (p.84) where the wooden teeth of the brake wheel drove the iron wallower through two staggered rows of teeth. The purpose was probably to reduce backlash and achieve greater silence of operation.

The study of auxiliary drive gears is also most rewarding, for these are of extreme variety. Sometimes a pair of

Hildenborough, Kent. *An eight-armed compass arm great spur wheel. The intermediate arms did not pass right through the upright shaft.*

Left: **Chislet, Kent.** *A clasp arm great spur wheel with auxiliary drive of cast iron close to the rim.*

Friston, Suffolk.
Photographed in its working days. The tail wheel which drove the tail stones underdrift via an upright shaft. The wooden teeth are held in position in the iron wheel by wedges between the shanks. The gear-like cam ring drove the jog scry.

well-made wooden bevel gears may be seen, as at Bardwell (p.76), or sometimes just an iron bevel and an iron ring on the great spur wheel. The drive to the wire machine at Hildenborough was from a bevel ring on the great spur wheel, and then through a pair of wooden bevel gears and finally by belt.

Very fine wooden skew gears were to be seen in many post mills, driving the auxiliary machines from the brake wheel. To eliminate the skew gear characteristic short shafts were sometimes used, as at Lowfield Heath, Surrey, when it was possible to mount the pinion on the radius. The teeth of a very few post mill brake wheels were also set at a slight angle from the radius to enable the wallower to be situated off centre. This allowed a larger pair of stones to be used on one side of the breast.

Two cast-iron windshafts, both found in Sussex, had mortices right through to facilitate the use of a compass arm brake wheel. One shaft was from Clymping smock mill, and the other from Sullington Warren post mill. There seems no reasonable explanation for this practice.

In order to compensate for wear and maintain a true relationship between the gears, adjustment for the footstep bearing and upper bearing of the upright shaft was provided. This is often achieved by using wedges to move the spindle or sprattle beams as at Whitstable, or a cast-iron bridging box where the brass bearing may be relocated with the aid of four set screws. Shiremark (p.84) shows an early type that used wedges directly against the bearing housing. An early form of maintaining the truth of the stone spindle is shown (p.84 below, left), the later bridging box being more convenient and positive in use.

While the casual observer may regard an eight-foot wooden windmill gear as crude, citing modern C.N.C. equipment as proof of the vast improvement in technology between then and now, there is, despite its size, nothing crude in the windmill gear. Workmanship was, and indeed had to be, of the highest quality with carefully chosen timber that had been air dried "in stick" (the trees sawn lengthways with spacers between each part to allow air circulation) for seven, or, ideally, nine years. The construction and tooth profiles had been worked out after centuries of empirical observation, and while modern calculation might produce an improved gear profile, its benefits would probably be indiscernible in use.

After the parts of a brake wheel had been sawn, using elm for the cants and fellows (the curved sections that cross the joints of the cants) and oak for the spokes, the blank gear would probably be laid flat and an arm known as a *trammel* set up to pivot from the exact centre. Using this, a line could be marked around the entire face of the gear at the estimated centre of the teeth. At this point a pair of dividers was opened up to the desired pitch and this was carefully walked round the line. In a perfect world everything works out to perfection, and the divider point lands exactly in the indent of its starting point. This can happen, and when it does everyone is duly delighted. Normally, it does not.

There are now two possibilities: opening or closing the dividers a little, a manoeuvre which will also change the pitch of the corresponding gear, or the moving of the centre line fractionally in or out. A very little movement of this line causes quite a difference in its length and so caution has to be exercised to avoid repeated marches along its length with the dividers. Once the spacing has been achieved, the mortices are marked out with great care on both sides, the trammel achieving

Shiremark, Surrey. *A heavy clasp arm great spur wheel on a wooden upright shaft. Note wedge adjustment for the footstep bearing of the upright shaft.*

a true radius and work taking place on both sides, care being taken to waist the work towards the centre so that this can be taken out to form a true parallel side when finishing the mortice.

The stone nut or wallower which meshes with the above is small enough to calculate its diameter mathematically, leaving enough oversize to turn a little off the face on a lathe until the dividers exactly match the circumference.

Spur gears are easier to calculate, but with these there is little alternative to altering the dividers to an exact pitch to suit the larger gear, after which the smaller gear has to be eased down to suit.

The teeth are now sawn to size, the shanks fitted carefully and the part which will form the tooth left square. The point of contact between the gears is called the pitch line and this is now calculated and with the gear mounted on its shaft, this is rotated against a fixed scriber to leave a mark at the pitch line. The scriber is now moved towards the root of the teeth to mark the drop line. This distance is either 10% of the tooth pitch or 10% of the space between the teeth. There is argument as to which is correct, an argument thrown into further confusion by measurement of existing period teeth; a watermill stone nut in my dining room seeming to have a drop line that relates to neither of the above measurements. In

Above: **Shiremark, Surrey.** *A wooden stone nut in engagement with the wooden great spur wheel. Note the wedge adjustment for the footstep bearing of the stone spindle.*

Above left: **Madingley, Cambridgeshire.** *The unusual staggered teeth on the brake wheel and wallower.*

84

**Horton Conquest,
Bedfordshire**. *A graft
shaft with mortice iron
great spur wheel.*

practice, the difference is not great and so the exact measurement may not be critical in use.

Where the drop line intersects the exact centre of the tooth, the point of the dividers is inserted, the other point being opened up to just register with the point where the pitch line leaves the far side of the adjacent tooth. An arc is now scored from here to the tip of the tooth and also on the tooth on the opposite side, the performance being repeated around the entire circumference of the wheel.

The millwright now produces a razor-sharp chisel and pares away the wood to this profile, running across the grain of the hard apple wood and leaving a smooth and true finish. Linseed oil is painted on to the surfaces and the gear is ready for many years work.

Look at the gear at Wingham (p.80). It is in elm, as is the brake band against the outer rim. The dowels are a perfect fit and the inner edge of the fellow has been chamfered for neatness. After years of hard use its parts have not moved – it is a work of art.

Where the drive is normally in one direction, as in the great spur wheel and stone nut, it is usual to have the teeth of the driven gear shorter as this reduces friction by loading the tooth as it heads towards disengagement rather than engagement. Obviously where items like fan gears are concerned, the drive is reversible and the tooth lengths equal.

I have made several wooden gears from scratch, using the above traditional method and hand tools, and can say that, as with every difficult task, the satisfaction of achievement is well worth the concentration; one's admiration of the men who made such things for a living being further enhanced by a greater understanding of their methods.

A morticed iron spur wheel is to be seen above. This is attached to a *graft shaft* where an iron extension has been joined to an older wooden upright shaft. This was sometimes used where there was a desire to move the stones down to a lower and wider floor, where there was more room to accommodate an additional pair, or where a change was made from overdrift to underdrift.

Part Three

Windmills in the Landscape

Saxtead Green, Suffolk. *Seen idling after virtually complete renewal by the late millwright Jesse Wightman, for the then Ministry of Works in the 1950s.*

CHAPTER 8

Windmills and their Surroundings

Most windmills are situated on hills or in other wind-catching positions. Flat areas are just as good for wind, and those mills in Lincolnshire or the fens worked as well as any. There is no explanation for the curious Shropshire practice of placing the tower mills of the area on the lower slopes of quite high hills. The mills must have worked well from some directions but have been completely sheltered from others. Vennington is an example, and there is even one empty tower at Cluddley, on the lower slopes of the famous Wrekin, which rises a matter of hundreds of feet above. This practice was not universal in the area, and some mills like Rowton and Homer may be seen for miles.

I was once standing in the field next to Keymer post mill. Mr Driver, the last miller, was reminiscing about times prior to 1912 when the mill had last worked. In those days one could see for miles in all directions and the wind blew free, although the easterly wind was best, the mill working really well, facing east. He waved his hand back towards the mill. "Of course, in those days this was all open." I looked about the mill and its environs. There were trees. Pleasant, sheltering, trees and hedges, but the place was no longer good for windmilling. In the words of a windmiller when I commented on the sycamore trees near my own mill, "trees are killers".

Saxtead Green mill has suffered the same fate. Once the surroundings were open, by the 1950s there were a few relatively small trees, but now the mill is becoming uncharacteristically screened. The buildings at Clayton mills were once entirely without shelter, but now a bank of low trees shields the fan when the mill is facing north-west, a potentially dangerous situation. There is, however, one advantage to the Clayton trees – they screen some of the unattractive modern

Stanford, Kent. *Another rare Kentish tower mill. At this time, 1960, it was worked by an engine. A little later the cap was mostly destroyed by the addition of an asbestos covering.*

Windmills, Sussex.

Clayton, Sussex. *The house in the centre has been replaced and the area is much grown-over with trees, but the post mill has been restored to working order. Restoration of the tower mill is awaited. (Old postcard)*

house from view. Once trees have grown, it is understandable that people are reluctant to cut them down, but trees and a working windmill are destined for an unhappy co-existence.

RAISING AND MOVING WINDMILLS

An unobstructed position with little turbulence caused by trees or buildings is very important, and several mills were jacked up bodily on to higher brick piers or bases. Tower mills were raised vertically from the original curb level (Northwood). The reasons for raising mills varied, but the most usual was that of growing trees or encroaching houses. At Drinkstone, Suffolk, the post mill stands on a mound while the smock mill is situated on the flatter ground a short distance away. It is interesting to note that, although the post mill mound reached to a fair height, this did not shelter the smock mill from the wind, and it worked perfectly when facing in this (northerly) direction. When the post mill started, however, it created turbulence, and the smock mill would not run satisfactorily. The miller of Sandwich smock mill, Kent, claimed that the turbulence from a shed built a few hundred yards to the south by the railway, had an effect on his mill. When the iron brake wheel spokes broke one day, proceedings were taken against the railway company. To prove the miller's point, a bonfire was started to windward of the shed and the smoke was duly observed eddying across to the mill. The miller's wind was originally protected, but as time elapsed it became evident that the miller's only real method of dealing with obstructions was either to raise the mill or move it to a better position.

Many wooden mills were moved in the past, either in one piece or in parts. Post mills were frequently moved about in this manner, when they were dragged on rollers or specially constructed sledges by as many as three dozen horses or oxen. Cross-in-Hand (p.6) has been moved twice. Smock mills were either sawn down each corner post and moved in sections, dismantled, or moved with the body on timber carts and the cap and machinery separately. This was not possible with tower mills, where the tower had to remain while the machinery and cap were fitted to a new tower at the new destination. Probably the most famous removal was that of the post mill at Clayton, Sussex, from a position at Brighton to the site it now occupies. This was achieved with a great number of oxen, and an old etching (which is often purported to show this move but is in fact of another Brighton

Bexhill, Sussex. *One of the wooden jacks that are said to have been used to raise the mill to higher brick piers in the 1860s.*

Northwood, Kent. *Demolished in 1960 to make room for a housing estate.*

mill) shows the sails off and the trestle resting on a wooden frame to which six rows of oxen are attached by traces. The mill body is braced to the frame by long timbers which extend down from the upper parts of the mill. When the size and weight of a windmill is considered, a removal would be an outstanding achievement even today with modern cranes and equipment, but in those times must have been an awe-inspiring occurrence.

The raising of a windmill must also have been quite nerve-wracking, especially for the luckless individuals who had the task of levering round the jack screws, their minds no doubt filled with thoughts of a quarterbar failure or of some calamity causing the mill to overbalance. A fine old jack is shown left and is said to have been used with others to raise Bexhill mill in the 1860s. The usual method of achieving this was to jack evenly beneath each crosstree close to the pier. The brickwork was increased by a few courses at a time until the mill had reached the desired height. This must have been a slow process, for the old lime mortar set rather slowly and there must have been considerable awareness that the centre of gravity had been reduced and that it might be necessary to lower the structure on to the piers in the event of a storm. The underside of the crosstrees at Windmill Hill mill still bear the imprint of four iron jack heads.

Windmill Hill, Sussex.
The second tallest post mill in the country, and the one with the largest body remaining. This very important mill is the only remaining English post mill that has never been restored. Subject to finance, a 100% authentic restoration is to commence.

Fornham St. Martin, Suffolk. *Two clockwise mills, both with strong weather to the sails. Note small size and early features of the post mill. Taken prior to 1882.* (Photographer unknown)

PAIRS OF WINDMILLS

Windmills were often found in pairs, which usually resulted from trade increasing to such a degree that the first mill could no longer cope. For this reason the mill which was added was often larger and much more modern that the original one.

This explains why most pairs are of different types and certainly different dates. The post mill at Clayton was added to a very old post mill which was itself demolished and replaced by the tower mill during the later nineteenth century. The single-storey roundhouse of this mill may still be seen at the base of the tower mill. The mill at Cross-in-Hand was also added to an old post mill, the roundhouse of which may still be seen. Examples of smock and post mills together were to be seen at Fornham and Drinkstone, Suffolk. and Outwood, Surrey. The remains of one such pair still exist in the grass at Great Hormead in Hertfordshire.

To see a pair of windmills at work must have been impressive, and people who have experienced this are few today, although an old Sussex carter could well remember such a sight at Clayton. How disappointing it is that nowhere can a pair of English mills be seen both in working order. Drinkstone smock mill is worthy of restoration too, for although the windshaft and machinery are missing, the finding of a suitable windshaft would not be difficult. This mill is very old, and is mounted on a wooden base which is reputed to have been a horse mill. Due to slackness in the joints between the cant posts and upright posts of the base the whole mill swayed slightly while at work.

Outwood, Surrey.
Before the loss of the smock mill. This had the tallest wooden 'smock' of any mill in the country and was a very fine mill. The post mill, which dates from 1665, was still at work when this picture was taken.

Great Hormead, Hertfordshire. *All that remained of the post mill and smock mill that once stood here in the 1960s. There is a collar just above the quarterbars that was used on some mills to transfer weight directly from the sheers.*

The mills at Fornham (p.92) were very interesting. Both were clockwise and both had strong weather to their sails, features of this part of Suffolk and east Cambridgeshire. According to Brian Flint in his book *Suffolk Windmills*, the post mill was moved away to some unknown destination prior to 1882. Note that this mill is small and has been updated by drilling the old wooden windshaft and poll end to accommodate patent sails. A fantail (*fly* in this part of England) has been fitted, but the cost of a roundhouse to enclose the trestle and provide storage has not been incurred. Both flies turn anti-clockwise, the opposite rotation to that of the sails, a tradition based on the deflection of the wind from the upper sail of a tower mill which could cause the mill to turn slightly out of wind unless the upper blade of the fly presented its edge to the deflected airflow. Obviously the lower sails would have the greatest influence on a post mill fly, but the tradition of counter rotation has persisted with only infrequent exceptions.

Drinkstone, Suffolk. *The very uncommon vertical side girt is seen to the left of the governors. The rather small early crowntree has been strengthened with a large iron casting on the underside.*

The situation of the only two remaining pairs of windmills is disappointing. The renovation of Clayton tower mill would be quite straightforward, for it only requires new work in the form of machinery, fan gears, shutters and striking gear. The mill is quite modern and probably used iron gearing, for which suitable patterns for casting might well be available due to the recent upsurge in windmill rebuilding. The site was somewhat spoilt during the 1960s by the demolition of the original mill house and the substitution of a rather unattractive modern building.

The site of Drinkstone windmills has not been spoilt directly, but the old gravel workings that surround it have become a huge and rather shabby pig farm which detracts from two very interesting mills in a pleasant part of Suffolk. It would be nice to think that we will not have to wait for Mr Lewis to complete his post mill as Asterly (more of which below), in order to once again see a pair of English windmills at work.

Silverhill, Sussex. *Lost to housing development in the early 1960s. This mill worked for much of the 1930s and was still part of the milling business when this photograph was taken in about 1959/60.*

Oldest Remaining Mills

Almost certainly the oldest remaining mill is that at Bourn in Cambridgeshire. This post mill is small in size and is original even to the open trestle and pent roof. This mill has, fortunately, been preserved since the 1930s when it was proved that it was already in existence in 1636. The oldest dated mill is that at Pitstone Green in Buckinghamshire, which has the date 1627 inscribed within. There seems little doubt, however, that Bourn mill in fact antedates this structure. The oldest dated post mill in working order is that at Outwood, Surrey, which worked from 1665 to the early 1960s when the miller, Mr Jupp, retired. Fortunately it was bought by two brothers who, until recently, continued to run the mill for demonstration purposes, the interior being open to view for a small charge. One of the oldest windmills to work into recent times was that at Drinkstone, Suffolk, which has vertical side girts which engage with joints on the upper and lower side girts (p.94). This is the oldest form of construction, and is similar to Bourn in this respect.

Some later post mills also used this form of construction which cannot be relied upon as absolute proof of extreme age. Drinkstone mill has had a varied life, the late Mr Clover, the miller, telling me that the original buck (body) was square and only nine feet across. It has also been extended in both the breast and the tail, one theory being that it has been turned end for end, although Mr Clover was sceptical about this. The result is that the post is central and the mill rather out of balance, causing it to be a little "headsick" (lower at the breast); a "tailsick" windmill leans backwards. The central position of the post also causes more swaying while at work than is experienced in most post mills. To demonstrate this to me, Mr Clover once gripped one of the doorposts and, by throwing himself from side to side, succeeded in swaying the entire mill, the joints creaking in protest.

Some areas were less inclined to change and accept new ideas than others, with the result that their windmills appeared older than was in fact the case. Some older mills have clockwise sails, although Burgh-Le-Marsh, Lincolnshire, is a clockwise five-sailed mill – a feature quite out of keeping with its other Lincolnshire characteristics. The great majority by far had anti-clockwise sails, and second-hand stones have to have the dressing cut in the reverse direction when used in a clockwise mill like Drinkstone. Unless the stone-nut is forward of the brake and tail wheels (and they seldom were) the stones turn in the same direction as the sails when viewed from above. When an upright shaft is used, as was always the case in tower and smock mills and was also found in many post mills, the rotation is the opposite to that of the sails. For this reason tower millstones could be used in a clockwise post mill without re-dressing.

New Buildings

Another and irreversible problem is that of housing development. Windmills were frequently situated on the edge of towns and villages and these expanded to surround the mill like a flow of volcanic lava. Delce mill, Rochester, and Silverhill mill, St Leonards, Sussex (p.95) are two examples. Both have been demolished, the first immediately after the Second World War and the last in 1963. The houses took first the wind and then the mill itself.

The same problem presents itself today with Downfield mill, Soham, once again at work, but surrounded by housing, the entrance being between two

Burwell, Cambridgeshire. *Bad planning – the mill is now in a housing estate.*

Soham, Cambridgeshire. *Bad planning – the mill is swamped by houses.*

bungalows at the end of a cul-de-sac. The nearby Burwell mill has suffered the same problem, this mill is also in working order, but now on a grassy patch in a housing estate.

When Lowfield Heath mill was moved to a new site at Charlwood, the argument was put to me that the site was too valuable for the mill to remain. This is utterly spurious. When land is occupied by an historic building, it is merely unavailable for other purposes. To believe otherwise is to place the Tower of London, Buckingham Palace and many London churches in jeopardy. These buildings are the heritage of future generations. We, their temporary custodians, should do all within our power to pass them onward, not only intact and unsullied, but with their environs conveying as much as possible the majesty of the building and the rural air of its surroundings. Great care should be exercised in granting planning consent close to a windmill.

Right: **Swaffham Prior, Suffolk.** *Bad planning – overshadowed by a vast water tower.*

Above: **Oare, Kent.** *One of the rare tower mills of the area. A secondary upright shaft drove more stones from the great spur wheel. Now destroyed by a house conversion.*

Left: **Over, Cambridgeshire.** *Bad planning – the mill is menaced by a gigantic aerial.*

Above: **Chalton, Hampshire.** *One of the rare Hampshire windmills photographed in the late 1950s. Regretably now house-converted.*

Right: **Stickford, Lincolnshire.** *A complete mill in the 1960s, the windshaft and other parts were removed to restore a house-converted mill in Rutlandshire, leaving this little mill devastated.*

CHAPTER 9

Local Traditions & Variations

Kent

A land of tall smock mills with caps similar to post mill roofs. Shuttered sails and a rocking lever, when the sails were patent, were common. Square brick bases were frequent and broad stages were very common indeed. Fan stages were of an individual type, inclined upward and quite lightly built and had fans with six or eight blades, well out from the fan star. The blades were small and the fan appeared rather sparse. Spring sails were often used, even in later times and on mills like Woodchurch which even had a hollow iron windshaft ready for patent sails.

Smock mills were the absolute speciality and tower mills quite scarce. Relatively few post mills survived into photographic times, a few in the Romney Marsh area being fitted with roof fantails, otherwise hand turning was the norm. Barham mill is proportionately and technically the archetypal Kentish windmill.

Rolvenden, Kent. *Restored as a memorial during the late 1950s. The well-known millwright and enthusiast Vincent Pargeter is seen standing on the poll end.*

Barham, Kent. *The sails were idling in a fresh breeze. This mill was sadly burnt down during the winter of 1969-70.*

Halvergate Marshes, Norfolk. *A partly restored drainage mill.*

Debenham, Suffolk. *Demolished in the early 1960s, this mill was owned by the same family as Framsden mill nearby. The cost of raising the post mill was nearly the same as building this new windmill.*

Madingley, Cambridgeshire. *A midlands type of post mill with the roundhouse roof turning with the body. This mill was moved from Huntingdonshire during the early 1930s.*

Sussex

On the whole, a mixed county with a special type of pepper-pot shaped cap on the tower mills. Smock mills seemed to favour the Kentish shape of cap. Many shuttered sails were used and could be of either spring or patent type. A wide leading board was often used for about the first two-thirds of the leading edge, the tip having shutters. Instead of standing out on the front of the whip, the triangles which operated the shutter bars were frequently found on the side of the stock. The spider thus had a rather twisted look when viewed from the ground.

The post mills were large, often with the tailpole fantail already mentioned. The breasts of these mills had a very pronounced point which aided air-flow from the sails. Most drove two pairs of stones, head and tail.

Fan stages were large and horizontal, the fans often with five blades that crowded close to the centre. Sheet metal covering, especially of post mills, was also a Sussex characteristic.

Surrey

So few mills remain in this county that it is not really possible to draw many conclusions. The evidence of old photographs certainly seems to indicate, however, that most of the smock mills at any rate had Kentish-type caps. A plentiful supply of water exists in this county, which encouraged the use of water mills. This, and the close presence of London, may help to explain the marked absence of windmills within the photographic past. Several post mills had stones side by side in the breast, an unusual feature south of the Thames.

Fulbourn, Cambridgeshire. *A clockwise smock mill with some vertical boarding and sails with very strong weather. This mill has since been restored.*

Somerset and the South west

Very few mills remain in these parts, but the Somerset type is the most common and was usually a vertical tower of fairly large diameter. The caps were large and based on the rectangular pattern with steeply sloping rafters. A wheel-and-chain luffing gear was usual. These mills were rather primitive in design and normally had common sails. The last to work was Ashton mill, which ceased in 1927.

Essex

This county had a mixture of types of mill and did not appear to have a very distinctive type of its own. The ladder fantail was found on several post mills. Being close to Suffolk, there was considerable influence from this direction and many sophisticated post mills were built. Single shuttered patent sails were in evidence with fairly narrow leading boards. Waltham Holy Cross probably represents the most southerly application of the ladder fantail in England.

Suffolk

Here the post mills were of a very individual type, being tall and narrow, often on very tall brick-built roundhouses. The breasts were frequently curved with the

104

boards bent round. Two pairs of stones side-by-side in the breast were also common, and shuttered sails were usual and were likely to be of the patent type. The timbers were often surprisingly small in section. Tower mills often seem to have had a rather tall beehive-shaped cap. Caps certainly tended to be round. Smock mills were uncommon. Here the post mill was developed to the highest standard in the world. Three or even four pairs of stones were often found together with additional pairs engine driven in the roundhouse. Double shuttered sails, a ladder fantail, a tall buck and a roundhouse of several stories are the features of the classic Suffolk post mill. The post mills to the west tended to be lower, sails having more acute weather and sometimes turning clockwise.

Norfolk

Tower and drainage mills were common here, and had a very distinctive type of boat-shaped cap which is best described as a more streamlined Kentish design. Rack-and-pinion operated striking gear with a pole to steady the chain was usual. Post mills have either a ladder fantail or the Sussex type mounted on the tailpole. The bucks were low, but quite large in floor area, the sole remaining example being at Garboldisham near the Suffolk border.

Cambridgeshire

This county contains some very interesting mills indeed, many being of a rather individual type. The common factors are few, but caps tended to be of a special pointed type, rounded in pattern with vertical boarding. The fantails had vertical fly posts which projected well above the small horizontal fan stage at the rear. The fans were large, and braces passed from the fly posts to the top of the cap. Vertical boarding was sometimes found on the smock mills.

Quite a number of smock mills were built in this county. A remarkable number of clockwise mills were built to the east, the angle of weather being very strong indeed.

Lincolnshire

This county achieved the peak of tower mill design with tall towers which had attractive ogee-shaped caps. The cross was the most common method of sail attachment, while patent sails were numerous. A rocking lever was used to operate the striking gear. Fantails were most outstanding, with inclined fly posts braced to the small fan stage. A hand rail is provided along the side of most fly posts for use by the miller while maintaining the fan gears and bearings. Fans were quite large with about eight blades. Machinery was often of iron and very modern. Multi-sailed mills were found here in considerable numbers, the county currently boasting working mills in all categories up to eight, and two each of five and six sails.

The North-east

Again, tower mills predominate, showing a strong Lincolnshire influence. Roller reefing sails were sometimes found in Yorkshire, a county that has contained quite a number of windmills. The last post mill, at Skirlaugh, was demolished during the Second World War. A feature of these mills was the attachment of the roundhouse roof to the mill body, the whole turning as one unit.

The Midlands

An area showing considerable influence from the surrounding counties, the tower mills of the east showing a Lincolnshire influence, whereas those of the west were more primitive. The post mills were quite outstanding with many special features. Breasts were often flat, and the breast beam straight with its ends resting on a forward projection of the upper side girts. When standing by the breast beam on these mills it is often possible to see a gap of several inches or more between the beam and the weatherboarding of the breast. A curb was also often seen on the trestle or roundhouse wall. The roundhouse roof also frequently turned with the body. Hurst frames were common, with two pairs of stones side-by-side in the breast of the spout floor. The framing was of large timbers with less diagonal bracing than was seen in the East. A very few in the extreme south of the area had three crosstrees and six quarterbars. These post mills seem to have had a remarkable resistance to the weather, for many old photographs show the mills still standing with virtually no boarding remaining. The use of a curb and oak framing may be an explanation.

Lancashire

In this county many tower mills were built. The towers were often white with black caps of a rectangular pattern. Shuttered sails were common, as was a cross to mount them. Fantails were high with sloping fly posts. None of the primitive post mills remains. A feature of these post mills was the extension of the body by using panniers, as seen at Hambleton mill.

Wales and the Marches

Primitive tower mills were of the usual type with wheel-and-chain luffing gear and common sails. Windmills are very scarce in the area and the majority of those that remain are just empty towers.

Anglesey

A considerable number of tower mills with wheel-and-chain luffing gear and common sails were found here. The caps were rectangular with slightly curved sides and tarred black. The mill at Llandeusant has recently been restored to working order, the only complete mill in the area.

These remarks only apply in general, and it is impossible to be dogmatic on any point. Each windmill was constructed individually, and no two are alike in more than the main features. A millwright might incorporate his own ideas, or even travel to a distant county, returning with some idea quite out of keeping with the local traditions. There are several examples of this, one being the Lincolnshire-pattern East Blatchington pumping mill, Sussex. Another was Horringer post mill, Suffolk which had a tailpole fantail.

The post mill was the first type of windmill and the poll end the earliest form of sail attachment. For this reason the existence of either in a county like Lincolnshire or Lancashire was more a mark of resistance to change than eccentricity.

Hambleton, Lancashire. *Seen at work on a breezy day in the late 1870s. Note the pannier extensions and typical small roundhouse.* Thomas Wade, author's collection.

Horringer, Suffolk. *A clockwise post mill near Bury St Edmunds. The sails have acute weather and there is a tailpole fan. The framing on the breast is to guard people from the sails.* Photographer unknown.

Part Four

Restoration and Replication

Chapter 10

The Post-War Years

After the Second World War the decline in the remaining working windmills was rapid. These mills were all worked seriously as part of the miller's business, and as their owners died or a stock became weak they stopped for good. The shortage of timber caused by the war also resulted in several sound mills being destroyed. One method used by millers to keep their mills working was that of obtaining second-hand sails from derelict mills. These were altered as necessary and put to work for a few more years. The supply of second-hand sails gradually dried up, and the only alternative was a new set. The cost usually prohibited this, and after working with only one pair for a while, an engine took over.

Engines had been used for auxiliary power since the coming of practical steam engines during the 1800s, and many old photographs show a tall chimney rising from a Victorian brick building beside the windmill. A pulley may often be seen projecting through the side of a post mill or from the tower of a smock or tower mill. This enabled a portable steam engine to be brought to drive the stones in a period of calm. A drive by bevel ring on the great spur wheel was usual in most mills, but some post mills had a pair of iron bevel gears on the stone spindle. Keymer post mill had this arrangement, an engine being kept in an adjacent shed and the mill turned in this direction when its services were required.

A few teeth were designed for removal on many brake wheels, which allowed the wallower to be rotated from beneath without revolving the sails. A large number of post mills had the engine drive to a pair or more of stones in the roundhouse.

Steam eventually gave way to gas or oil engines which may occasionally be seen *in situ* to this day. These engines had one very large horizontal cylinder with exposed conrod, big-end and crankshaft. The crankshaft carried one or two flywheels of about four feet diameter and a belt pulley. The belt often passed into the mill through a short tunnel or passage, which helped to isolate the engine shed from the milling process. The exhaust was discharged through a very large diameter vertical pipe with a most distinctive chuffing note.

The use of these engines has probably prolonged the existence of many mills, and has certainly enabled those that have worked by wind since the war to continue. The drives were so varied that they defy description in detail, but the lack of guards around both belt run on points and gears has caused several untimely deaths. Unfortunately, many auxiliary engines have been broken up for scrap, and steam engines are particularly scarce.

The decline in the numbers of working windmills continued, and their scarcity at last provoked an awakening of interest in windmill preservation. The 1950s saw real progress, with several working mills receiving financial assistance when repairs were required. The most usual form of preservation was that undertaken by local and county councils. Beneficial as it is to preserve windmills in any form, these works, although praiseworthy, were frequently of poor quality. In many cases millwrights were not used and, when they were, they were sometimes

Shipley, Sussex. Restored to working order in 1958.

111

Wingham, Kent. *Now destroyed, the sails have been re-erected on Sandwich smock mill.*

dictated to by borough surveyors who knew nothing of windmills.

A typical restoration of the mid-to-late 1950s usually concerned itself only with the aesthetic aspect of a local windmill. A set of sails and a coat of paint was all that concerned the restorers, and it was immaterial to them whether a side girt could be half broken through or a cant post in two halves. In the concern for sails, insufficient attention was frequently paid to making the mill watertight. The rain penetrated to the dry interior timbers which, once exposed, can rot surprisingly quickly.

Councils have been, until recently, the most prolific repairers of mills, but it is rather unfair that they should receive all the blame for the damage that has been done. Some councils have carried out very good repairs which could almost be termed restorations. The secret of these is that they have employed millwrights for all the work and not just for the bare minimum.

About 1960 I witnessed the final phase of the restoration of a certain windmill. A millwright had been commissioned to deal with the new sails, which were excellent. The council had repaired the body, using scaffolding which surrounded the mill for some time. The paint had been renewed, but it had been applied to an exterior which had been patched with tin and hardboard. In the tail it was possible to push a finger right through the rotten weatherboarding. Inside the mill the shutters for closing the windows were still lying; they had not been replaced ten years later.

No public body would restore the interior of an ancient castle but leave a leaking roof. Why then should they do what amounts to the same thing to an equally historic monument? The answer is twofold; lack of knowledge and lack of money. If money is short it is well worth restoring the tower or body to a perfect condition, leaving the sails to a later date.

The lesson concerning millwrights seems to be penetrating, but that concerning the use of poor materials is not. Many readers, who have recently observed that the soft pine stock of a local preserved windmill has snapped after only ten years' use, were probably amazed to note that a stock lasted forty years in the past. The answer is simply that the stocks were made of pitch pine or other excellent timber, and stocks of this material should last equally long today. Any council contemplating repairs to a windmill should first consult a millwright as to the correct materials for the job. These should then be specified when tenders are sent out. The use of tenders is not always beneficial, as the cheapest work is not necessarily the best.

Naturally enough, most preservers prefer to own the freehold of a windmill and, with public money in use, local authorities are no exception. The problem is that with all the sub-committees and official delays involved, the windmill may deteriorate much more than need have been the case. There are at least two cases of windmills collapsing during negotiations which took several years. In more than one instance the council has settled for a very long lease at a very low rent. The standard of repair is becoming better, and it is to be hoped that public bodies will in future concern themselves not only with the exterior, but also with the interior and the small buildings which often surround a windmill. These buildings were often as old as the windmill and were as much a part of the whole as the machinery. Careless repair has led to much machinery being ripped out and many small granaries and barns being demolished.

BEFORE THE TOURISTS

I was recently talking to a very knowledgeable and enthusiastic owner of a windmill. To my surprise he said he had never been in a working post mill, that is to say, one run by an old-time miller and that worked for trade. The reason was time and circumstance. Cross-in-Hand mill ceased work in June 1969 and Drinkstone not long afterwards. Even if one were old enough to have experienced these mills at work, one would have had to be there when there was a wind and the mill was running. For this reason I never saw Friston mill grinding by wind, despite visiting it twice during its working days.

Willingham, Cambridgeshire. *The last smock mill to work in the county, it ceased in the early 1960s.*

Why, you may ask, do I make the distinction between a mill working for trade and one that opens at the weekends in summer and grinds the odd bag of meal? The reason is that the atmosphere of the two is incomparable.

Cross-in-Hand mill was like a car that had been repaired just enough to pass the Ministry of Transport test for year after year, but, like all its compatriots that worked for trade, it had character.

Stelling Minnis was another windmill with character. It was not an old mill, having been built in 1866 on the site of a post mill and was quite small, the brick base extending to only a few feet in height and the fan stage with just enough room for one man to crouch beneath the blades. Externally the mill was quite smart, the paintwork of the tower having been regularly renewed by the old millwrighting firm of Holman, who built the mill and dressed the stones to the end.

There were only two sails, the stock of the other pair having broken when it hit a cradle that had been left on the stage by the millwrights. There were a number of trees in the vicinity and these and the fact that only two sails remained meant that the old engine in the adjacent shed had quite frequent use. This engine, though, had its problems, the most tiresome being that the flywheel continually came loose, necessitating a drift being inserted through a specially-cut hole in the outside wall and held in place against the key while an assistant struck it with a sledge hammer. A lesser difficulty was one caused by the freezing of the cooling water tanks during a heavy frost. The use of windpower was not straightforward either, for part of the decking of the stage was missing and if the cap turned so that the striking chain hung over one of these spaces, then the shutters could only be opened or closed from a ladder. Using the brake also had its awkward aspects for the rope had frayed from constant lashing in the wind and latterly this was out of reach even from the stage. To stop the sails it was necessary first to fetch a ladder and unhitch the weight from the chain, and then to climb up through the mill to the cap and lower the brake lever.

To enter the mill, one passed through one of the cills, the lack of a continuous linkage of these having no apparent ill-effect on so low a base. Inside, sacks were heaped to the ceiling, the floor thick with dust, mice scattering if taken by surprise. Upstairs, two doors gave access to the stage, the light, if these were closed, struggling to enter through windows caked with dust internally and streaked with tar splashes without. On the stone floor space was restricted, the two pairs of stones having different vats, one octagonal, the other round. Both the peaks and the burrs were in use to the end, Mr Davison, the miller, using a novel method of stemming the flow of excess grain into their eyes, a problem caused by mice entering the shoe when the mill was at rest – each carried an old hat thrust into the exit.

The bin floor was not really a floor at all, for the bins filled the entire area, the ladder being hinged back with the aid of a counterweight in order to provide a route for sacks to be brought up by the hoist.

When at work the mill creaked and vibrated although there was not the excitement of a post mill, but it did have the most wonderful atmosphere. The whole place, but especially the interior, had an overwhelming aura of the past and of rural life in those times.

Drinkstone mills also had this feeling, from the worn gravel track that led from the smock mill to the post mill, the ancient railway carriage used as a workshop, the spare stock (I believe from Rougham Common) under a covering of corrugated iron, to the cramped, meal-smelling interior of both windmills. Business was carried on in an unhurried way and there was a sensation of timeless entity within the farming community.

Tower mills were more stately, but the movement of lorries loading and unloading, farmers placing and collecting orders and the general activity of people at work was the same. The visiting enthusiast was uncommon and was almost universally left to climb where he pleased and talked to about windmilling, the days of horse transport, or traction engines, as work or disposition dictated. Pakenham mill, as it was when I first knew it, had two moods. The first, when the small stones were running from the distorted internal iron gear on the great spur wheel,

was one of a grinding, roaring sound that filled the whole tower when the speed increased and the other, when one of the larger pairs of stones was grinding, of silent grandeur. I have a pleasant memory of spending some time out on the cap gallery, one summer evening, the cap facing north and the sails rising past me, massive and white, in a light breeze.

A windmill did not necessarily have to be working by wind in order to retain something of the feel of a working mill and those like Silver Hill, Barnham, the roundhouse at Syleham and even the New Mill at Northbourne, with its single pair of engine-driven stones on a lower floor, still had the polished woodwork, the smell, the dust and, from time to time, the rumble of millstones.

Thornham Magna post mill may have ceased work in 1942, but fifteen years later the roundhouse was piled with sacks of meal that had been delivered there by lorry for distribution to

Thornham Magna, Suffolk. *Photographed in 1958.*

Woolpit, Suffolk.
Before its collapse in 1963. The left hand breast corner post is beginning to fail.

Inset: **Bexhill, Sussex.**
Known as Downs Mill, this collapsed in the 1960s.

the various holdings on the estate. The only way up into the mill was via the quarter bars and a sack trap, the activity in the roundhouse a strange contrast with the buck, the interior of which was complete, but with rain pouring through gaping holes in the boarding (p.115). There was a tremendous forward lean which ballast in the tail had failed to cure, the floor sloping away towards the breast in a manner that suggested the imminent demise of the whole structure. The windshaft was wooden and, as I recall, round in section, the two pairs of stones in the breast retaining all their furniture.

The upper steps of the ladder had all gone and the rather lightly-built fly had collapsed into the stinging nettles and brambles. When I was there, there was a melancholy air about the place, perhaps brought on by the late evening sunshine that came in through the boarding and showed the green algae on the floorboards that had once been worn and shone by generations of millers' feet.

The wife of the last miller still lived in the mill house and she talked about the mill, including recounting how her son had dashed up the track to the mill "when the wind got on the back of the sails". I was mistaken when I said in the first edition of this book that this mill had been demolished. It was set on fire by vandals in 1959. A sad loss of a very complete Suffolk post mill.

Back in the last days of this mill there were many such derelict windmills to be seen. Frequently the last miller or their family lived in the nearby house and as strangers seldom visited, there was almost universally a pleasant welcome. Men like old Mr Gaston from Nonnington in Kent formed a direct link with the days of grinding by wind and his windmill too, for despite being without cap or sails, it had worked with an engine for many years and was just as it had been last used, sacks where they had last been hung and the big single cylinder engine in the adjacent shed clean and ready for action, the building still smelling of oil and fuel.

Visiting a windmill in those days was something of an adventure, for there was always something to discover, ladderless floors to be reached, or rotting chasms to be bridged. Sometimes the mill would be little more than mouldering timbers in a forest of brambles, or the door only accessible via a bed of stinging nettles.

Bexhill post mill was derelict, but securely locked. Mr Hoad, the owner, had refused access for many years, but one day Vincent Pargeter and I somehow won him over and we were allowed inside. What we found was a totally complete mill with all manner of artefacts from its working days lying about. Sacks, dressing tools, staff, mousetraps, a fine set of old wooden bushel and parts thereof, measures and an old wooden jack that was said to have been used to raise the trestle to higher piers. The structural condition was terrible, with the left hand breast corner post having failed and the breast beam having separated from its joint. The prick post and breast were rotten and much of the weight of the windshaft and three remaining sails was being taken by the forward quant. Two light chains held the breast beam back to the tail beam, but apart from a small iron bracket that held the lowest sail to the roundhouse wall, no other remedial work had been done. The last time I went inside, Mr Hoad asked me to check the chains "because last time I saw them, they were like harp strings". I later reported that one had broken. He looked thoughtful, but said that it would be all right. Two or three months later there was a strong south-westerly wind. A bang sounded from the mill and someone in the mill yard watched the entire breast cantilever

outwards, the windshaft destroying a caravan that had been parked below, and the rest of the mill falling all around.

A similar fate befell Woolpit mill, the same corner post having rotted through and swung outwards, virtually the entire weight of the windshaft being taken by the forward quant. After Mr Elmer, the miller, died in the early 1950s, nothing was done to the mill, and when I first gained entry in 1958 the bins still contained the last decaying batch of grain. At that time the corner post had been strengthened, but was showing signs of weakness, the condition worsening and the breast falling apart until the final collapse in 1963 (p.117).

Alford, Lincolnshire. *This mill is still at work and has never ceased working from new.*

MUSEUM WINDMILLS

I have a fairly firmly held rule: "do not go inside a windmill that you remember as a working mill, once it has been museumised". Not long ago I broke this rule and went inside Stelling Minnis mill. This had been taken over by the council after the death of Mr Davison and had been renovated with a full set of sails which contained a scattering of shutters. A regrettable, non-authentic additional hand rail had been fitted to that on the stage, but the mill generally looked rather good. It IS good; a strong, preserved windmill which could very easily be put to work.

The inside is tidy with nothing out of place and no speck of dust to be seen. The sacks have gone, the smell has gone and the mice have nowhere to hide. There are useful displays to inform the uninformed. Notices abound and souvenirs can be bought. The atmosphere has gone. The soul has gone. The whole place is dead. The mill is capable of work, but it is not a working mill, nor does it remotely feel like one.

Sarre, Kent. *As it was in 1960 and, now, silhouetted against the evening sky after ceasing work for the day. This mill is fully restored and in constant work.*

There are many mills like this, frequently owned by local authorities or run by committees or groups. They are in good order, some are more authentic than others, the sails may occasionally be seen turning and all are the result of extraordinary worthwhile work. They are, however, museums.

At Sarre mill and Boston and Alford mills, a strenuous effort has been made to avoid notices and the paraphernalia of a museum. These mills work. They also allow visitors to view them while at work. A full complement of shutters is fitted and the sails turn fast to maximise the output for a given wind. At Sarre, grain is deliberately bought from the merchant in sacks in order to promote a traditional feeling, and is even transferred from paper to hessian sacks for the same reason.

Some years ago there was a brisk wind on a summer weekend and I decided to visit a recently restored post mill which I though might be working. I was rather early and found a man in attendance. I asked if the mill would be running and he astonished me by replying that there was too much wind. Too much wind? Try telling that to a real windmiller! Only in the severest of gales would the mill be brought to a halt, for with the cloths furled or the shutters open and several pairs of stones in gear, most gales could be ridden out. On this particular day there was no more than a fresh breeze and the sails contained only a scatter of shutters.

I then asked if I could go up into the mill, but he said "no". He had not put out his notices and that anyway he would wait for enough people to arrive and give me a guided tour. This was notable by its half accuracies and I learnt several things that would have surprised the old-time millers. A great pity, for a couple of years after, someone with no more than a casual knowledge visited the mill and later repeated the same misinformation.

The problem of too much wind was quoted as an excuse for not working at another museum mill and it seems that many custodians are nervous of their charges and have no idea how hard the mills were normally worked. I have mentioned Cross-in-Hand mill, but Mr Ashdown was not alone in making full use of the wind, for Mr Bob Wright, son of the late Mr Reynolds Wright, told me that his father once set Friston mill to work while the millwrights, who were re-cogging a gear, went to lunch. He engaged the left-hand breast stones and ground one ton of beans during the hour that they were away. To give some idea of the output, this equates to changing a one hundredweight sack at the meal spout every three minutes. Equally, Mr Hobbs of Sarre tells tales of how the last miller at Chillenden used to pile his open trestle windmill with sacks of grain and meal and run it so hard that "many people came out of there a lot faster than they went in". The mill was rather headsick and on the south-west side there was a shallow trench to enable the fast-turning spring sails to clear the ground.

One day in 1993 300 people visited the rather obscure post mill at Nutley. At a more prominent mill I have heard figures of 2,000 visitors in a weekend. With such a crush of humanity in a relatively small building there could be considerable difficulty in working and in a post mill there could well be a problem of safety due to the proximity of the moving gears. For this reason, at Clayton and Mountnessing grinding is carried out on days when there is no public access. With the burgeoning enthusiasm for mills and milling this arrangement could become more common and the true enthusiast who wishes to see the mill grinding will have to make private arrangements to see the mill at work.

Boston, Lincolnshire. *Fully restored and in constant work. A town mill in surroundings little changed since the beginning of the century.*

CHAPTER 11

Repair Work

When restoring a windmill it is of importance that the work is a perfect reproduction of that originally found. Typical examples of very bad reproduction have been where the maximum weather of the sails is towards the tip, where the weather is constant, or where the sail is just a flat framework. Such careless work is very bad indeed, and is usually the result of work by local builders or council workers who know nothing of the construction of a windmill. Errors of this type have become scarce in recent years, and it is to be hoped that the offending owners will replace these disgraces as soon as possible. One extreme example of this kind of work carried two clockwise and two anti-clockwise sails!

A more subtle type of mistake is that of changing the type of joint used between the various timbers. This again is uncommon today, but in the past side girts have been recessed into the corner posts and joined by iron plates without using a tenon. This is just as strong as the original, but when it is realised that the work may well be examined in 500 years time and believed to be original, the mistake is placed in true perspective. When making a joint or fashioning a piece of timber this fact should be imprinted upon the mind. If the timber to be replaced is missing, then the joints and construction should be as near as can be judged by using local windmills as an example. Should these all have been demolished, then the same type of joint should be used as in other areas. The recording

Nutley, Sussex. *During restoration, 1970.*

Nutley, Sussex. *The start of a new era – a trestle completely renewed by a group of enthusiasts.*

Cranbrook, Kent. *The dreadful anachronistic steel Dutch-type sails as fitted in 1959/60. It is to be hoped that these will be replaced as soon as possible by proper white-painted sails and stocks.*

of the design of the various joints has not been carried out very systematically, for many enthusiasts feel that they cannot waste expensive film on such matters. The exposure of such places as the crowntree ends is not common, and when they are visible, these probably display a joint so neglected that they do not demonstrate the type well.

Some people argue that if windmills were still in commercial use today the old millwrights would have adopted the materials and methods of the time. This is undoubtedly true, but the fact remains that windmills are a relic of the past, and have been relegated to the ranks of castles and old sailing ships. Like vintage cars, windmills can still be used in the original manner, but this is no reason why they should not be maintained to high standards of condition and originality.

In Holland, where windmills were very common, a special design of sail evolved just before the Second World War. This consisted of a very long stock which also replaced the whip; the sail bars were morticed through in the normal way and the sails built up after the stock had been erected. This stock was often built out of steel plate. Cranbrook mill, Kent, was restored in 1960 and in spite of a very large sum of money being expended, was completely ruined by the addition of this type of sail. Apart from the practical disadvantage that the sails are now very close to the mill tower, this type of degradation should be avoided at all costs for the mill is no longer typical of either England or Holland.

The finest way to preserve a mill is to keep it at work, but, as this is not possible in a great number of cases, certain precautions have to be taken which are quite excusable. A windmill like that at Chillenden, which stands alone in a field, often receives the full attention of vandals. The pumping mill at Walberswick, Suffolk was completely burnt out in the late 1960s through the efforts of these people. To avoid damage of this type the lower windows are often boarded or bricked up and the door very securely locked.

The sail shutters are frequently removed to lessen wind-resistance in a tail-wind, a variation being the use of bare shutter frames when these were covered with canvas. Another excellent idea which is becoming more frequent in use is that of having only a few shutters in the sails; the post mill at Saxtead Green Suffolk (p.87) being an example. The owner of Barham smock mill, Kent (p.100) used an equally sensible arrangement in which he had a full complement of shutters only for about two-thirds of the way out from the heel. The last few bays were empty.

The fan is often erected in skeleton form, also to lessen wind-resistance. An early example is at West Kingsdown, Kent, although this originally had seven blades rather than the current six. This mill illustrates the beginnings of belief in restoration to an original form, for the fan stage was completely missing before work commenced. The excellent mill at Argos Hill, Sussex, had the tailpole fantail replaced during the 1960s after it had lain neglected in the field for many years. The fan here also is of skeleton pattern, for with the mill unattended it is currently not required for turning purposes.

West Kingsdown, Kent. *Shortly after renovation in 1960.*

With such examples as these, it is to be hoped that other public bodies will follow by restoring the exterior of their mills as thoroughly and maybe also the interior. Excellent examples of restoration have been achieved by private individuals forming committees or trusts which raise money by means of public subscription, fetes, or other methods. The result is often very authentic, and may even be used for work. Clayton post mill was restored to full working order in the early 1980s by such a group, an example that has since been followed at other mills, the cost being surprisingly low in financial terms, but high in man (and woman!) hours.

ENTHUSIASTS

To most windmill enthusiasts a shell restoration is of little interest, for they are concerned with originality and the recording of windmills as they were constructed by millwrights and used by millers. A derelict Cambridgeshire smock mill is far more likely to receive a visit from such people than a hollow tower with a recent cap like Halnaker in Sussex.

Most dream of owning a real windmill and even working it, but usually have to be content with a model, which either spins merrily on the lawn or is used to demonstrate windmill construction in the sitting-room. One such enthusiast takes this to an extreme and even has salt-cellars made like small windmills. Some attain their ambition and either own a preserved example or restore a derelict mill to working order. Others with less finance join together in groups to carry out the complete restoration of a local mill.

Some quite remarkable work has been achieved in this way, for these people not only know what the result should be like, but also do not charge for their many hours of work. A complete rebuild can thus be found to have cost only a few thousand pounds.

One is often asked how and why one became interested in windmills. There seem to be three main routes; a local mill requires restoration and the individual becomes involved, a publicly open windmill is visited, or one is inspired in childhood.

Piers Hartley, the owner of Friston mill, remembers entering an unidentified working mill at the age of four, the impression lasting throughout his life. Vincent Pargeter became inspired at the age of eight, and I was taken for a walk past Clayton mills at the same age, being stunned by their size. The interest was compounded by a walk past Keymer post mill three years later, after which I remember telling my mother, as I climbed into bed that evening, how astonished I was by the sheer size of this rather short windmill.

Who could fail to be moved by a visit to a proper working windmill like Alford or Sarre? With such mills hard at work, the sails flashing past the windows, the cap quivering and creaking and dusty meal pouring from the spouts, is it surprising that the number of enthusiasts is growing?

WINDMILL PARTS

I was once standing on the site of Ashcombe six-sailed post mill. Nothing remained of either the mill or the adjacent granary. I started to search the bottom of the nearby hedge and found some pieces of millstone and then, lying part

Ashcombe, Sussex.
The Mill overlooked Kingston and was supposedly preserved at this time. Sadly it was allowed to collapse in 1916. Old postcard.

buried in the newly tilled field – a broken shutter crank. Is this all that remains of this mill? It is now labelled and preserved, for perhaps one day someone will research the design of shutter cranks or even try to produce a painstaking replica of this famous mill. For the identity of my broken crank to be somehow lost would surely be a crime.

It might be a good idea for those who have old windmill parts to make sure that their identity is recorded for posterity. As a matter of record, there is a mace in Punnetts Town mill that I purchased from the wreckage of Outwood smock mill and donated to the rebuild, and the post of a hollow post pumping mill supports the engine-driven stones at Saxtead Green. The Weatheringsett crowntree has already been mentioned, but not that some sail clamps from Tunstall mill were sawn up and used to extend the floor in Friston roundhouse. These are small things, but it is pleasing to think that some part of an old windmill still remains.

The vicinity of a windmill sometimes contains interesting old weathervanes or models and in 1958 Mr Wightman pointed out that the model post mill in the garden of Saxtead Green mill house was seventy years old. This is now preserved within a shed. The charming little tower mill that used to be beside Pakenham mill in the 1950s seems to have gone; it is hoped that that too has been preserved.

CHAPTER 12

—

Authenticity and Originality

There is a word much used in the world of antique cars: originality. Windmill Hill windmill is very original – it is almost untouched after one hundred years of idleness and every piece of timber within it, rotten or otherwise, was fashioned by the old-time millwrights. It is very original. Asterly windmill, on the other hand, is not at all original, but it is highly authentic.

A perfectly original windmill would be one that had never been altered or upgraded during its working life and had avoided the heavy-handed restorer. Such a mill would have to be a late one like Stone Cross, for most old mills show signs of alteration. Desirable as such a windmill might be, the restorer should definitely not try to return an old mill to the likely state of its first construction. There would inevitably be an element of conjecture and hence falseness about such a reconstruction. Besides, the process of evolution is an interesting feature to study and the newer machinery, individually made, is of great intrinsic merit.

At what stage, then, to paraphrase William Morris, should one "stay the hand of history"? My own view is that the line should be drawn at the stage of development reached when the windmill last worked by wind. If a very old post mill had a tailwheel and second pair of stones added; leave them. If an auxiliary oil engine was in place; leave that too. Do not revert from patent sails to commons and do not remove the fantail and go back to wheel-and-chain winding as was done a Halnaker before the War. The above are very obvious major changes, but what of those of a more subtle nature?

In later life Sussex post mills frequently carried a protective layer of flat sheet-steel nailed over the more picturesque weatherboarding. The restorer sees the layer of white paint beneath the metal and wonders how far he should turn back the clock. At Clayton there was corrugated iron on the breast and plain sheeting on the roof. Both were *in situ* when the mill last worked, but were destined for removal at the time of the major renovation planned in the late 1970s. I made the point strongly that the sheeting was part of the history of the mill and a compromise was reached; the particularly unattractive corrugated iron was removed, while the more characteristic smooth material was retained on the roof. I am not a lover of sheet metal, but it *is* a typical Sussex feature and Telham Hill, Clayton post, Cross-in-Hand, Argos Hill and Windmill Hill all displayed this sheeting into recent times. Windmill Hill probably owes its survival to the water resistant qualities of its iron coating, the white paint having long gone and the mill displaying red rust for very many years. Argos Hill mill has a covering of sheet metal on its roof. Before the Second World War this was painted white like the rest of the mill. At some later date red lead paint was used on this metal and the mill became red and white. Red lead is a very good preservative of ironwork, but the colour scheme has somehow stuck and the mill is no longer authentic.

So what exactly is authenticity? Authenticity is the replacement of damaged parts, like the broken side girts at Windmill Hill, with parts of identical dimen-

Medmerry, Sussex.
A crane hoisting the windshaft back into place after it had been half blown out. The cap was subsequently butchered into a plain dome.

Telham Hill, Sussex.
In the autumn of its life and after demolition in 1962.

sion and finish in the same material. If oak was used, then oak should be used again and the same for other types of timber wherever possible. Authenticity is also the splicing of partially damaged timbers and the plating of others like the sheers at Windmill Hill which have fractured due to the sinking of the rest of the mill body. In the case of this particular mill it would also involve the replacement of the missing stone furniture with copies of original items found in other comparable windmills. The standard of construction of this light woodwork should be good quality carpentry – cabinet maker standard is admirable, but incorrect.

Disappointingly, a number of non-authentic repairs have been carried out in recent times. A few come to mind.

The ghastly stocks-cum-whips are still in place on Cranbrook smock mill. It is to be hoped that this grotesque feature will be removed as soon as possible and that the new stocks and sail whips, together with various other parts of the mill exterior that have been painted black, will be restored to white, the colour of the mill when at work.

When I visited Icklesham post mill in the late 1950s, a non-operational fan had been fitted of a smaller diameter than the original. The ladder had been replaced with an affair of braced timbers and the wheels and tram frame leant

against this framing. The track that the wheels had once travelled was level. For some years restoration work has been slowly advancing and at last the mill was turning to wind. When I went up to the mill I was surprised to note that the fan was of the non-authentic smaller diameter and that a strange raised track had been built around the mill, the tram wheels being inclined and running against a tramway pitched towards the roundhouse wall. I asked the well-known windmill historian, Mr Frank Gregory, the layout of the track during the 1930s when the fan was in operation. Without hesitation he replied that it was flat. No doubt the idea of the pitched track is that it would receive some thrust from the tramwheels during a hurricane, but the mill is almost certain to settle forwards when the heavy spring sails are added at some future date and the tramwheels move towards the mill and out of engagement. Such a track would have been very tiresome to work with in the days of horses, for heavy waggons would have to pass over it and carters would be obliged to reverse their loads up to the roundhouse door. Horses never take kindly to moving backwards, and to ask them to do so while forcing the wheels of a laden waggon over such a raised track would be very difficult.

A similar situation exists at High Salvington. This mill and its immediate surroundings were used for many years as a tea room and garden. At some early point the original wooden roundhouse with vertically boarded sides was replaced with an octagonal brick affair, the floor of which covered the lower crosstree to provide a flat space for tables and chairs. In the mid-1950s the mill was original but decrepit, with two common sails in position, although major work was required. Most of the framing was replaced and a great deal of originality was lost. The airbricks to the underside of the roundhouse floor had become blocked many years before and the lower crosstree was seriously rotten. This was braced and the mill renovated to a reasonable external appearance.

Some years elapsed until further work was required, which was undertaken by a group of enthusiasts on behalf of the council, who are the owners. A great deal of work was carried out including the rebuilding of the trestle and replacement of the crowntree. Much effort has been expended upon inserting tenons into joints that had been assembled with the use of iron joining plates and the replacement of missing original parts. Happily the mill is now in working order and has ground grain.

The unhappy side of this tale, however, is the roundhouse. Apparently the replacement was designed by an architect with the intention of allowing greater air movement beneath the lower crosstree. The usual method of achieving this in

The workshops of E Hole and Son. *A set of sails and stocks is in the process of manufacture in 1959.*

a mill with very low brick piers is to have a step down onto the roundhouse floor. No so in this case. For some peculiar reason the area around the roundhouse was excavated and the ladder now rests upon a bank with steps rising from the roundhouse door to the level of the surrounding area. Waggons could not possibly be brought up to the roundhouse and men would have had to carry 20-stone sacks of flour up the steps and then hoist them onto the waggon. Needless to say, early photographs show level ground extending to the roundhouse.

It seems a shame that such non-authentic work will probably be demolished and replaced by future generations in a similar way to the replacement of the initial repair work at High Salvington. There is no substitute for authenticity, but the lesson is not being learnt as fast as one would wish.

Some despoilation has been carried out in the name of safety. At Saxtead Green there are some particularly unpleasant guards over all the moving parts, even including the slow-moving tram wheels, while Waltham mill in Lincolnshire has been butchered to the extent of fitting additional staircases so that each floor now has the non-authentic feature of two routes of access. It is to be hoped that in this age of bureaucracy, such errors will not multiply.

Quite a few smock and tower mills were fitted with electric lighting during their last years of activity. This could be termed an authentic feature, but should be replaced in a discreet manner. Regrettably this is often not the case and heavy conduits are used with bulky switches and sockets. Sometimes electric lighting is used in post mills with a detachable connection to the roundhouse. This is not authentic and can look very out of place. Candles and lamps were the original form of illumination for night working, but are a fire risk. The answer, surely, is in the use of modern rechargeable electric lamps. Anyway, visitors are usually ushered from the building well before darkness and my own mill must be the only post mill currently to work at night, so why bother with illumination?

Modern bricklayers use what is known at "bucket handle pointing". This is crude and fast and leaves the impression of a finger having been drawn along the joint. This type of pointing at once identifies new work and bricklayers should be instructed to use a trowel in the traditional manner and to follow the bonding of the original work.

Large section timber for such items as stocks is becoming increasingly hard to locate. Quite frequently the solution is found in box section steel stocks which are no heavier than the originals and are disinclined to break. In position they look very similar to the correct items. On the whole I am inclined against them. Windmills were originally timber constructions and should remain so. Replace one

High Salvington, Sussex. *During renovation in the 1950s. The side girl and the end of the crowntree can clearly be seen.*

Drinkstone, Suffolk. *A lost age. A candle holder by the breast meal spout.*

item with a fake of steel, then another, then the rest with fibreglass, and what does one have? Something that does not feel or behave the same as the original. The steel stock might well attract lightning and not act as a safety valve by breaking in an extreme circumstance. A better solution would be to use laminated timber. This is very strong and displays the characteristics of normal timber and can even be manufactured by the private individual.

There is an additional dimension to authenticity. Punnetts Town mill is not very authentic, neither is more than the tower original. It is, however, a very early restoration to working order. How then should future generations consider it – a major stepping stone in the history of this type of building, or something to be rebuilt as near as possible to its last working form?

To use antique motor cars as a simile: an original vehicle in good condition is regarded most highly in both aesthetic and financial terms; next comes an authentic restoration; then something that has been modified many years ago; after this, various states of nasty restoration, and finally, fakes. The car movement is parallel, but many years in advance of that of the windmill. It might give a guide to future attitudes. Where does Punnetts Town fit?

CHAPTER 13

Restoration to Working Order

An outstanding piece of work was commenced by Mr Dallaway on Punnetts Town mill, Sussex (p.136) in 1947. This smock mill had been left as an empty tower by his father, the cap had been removed and the interior was used for storing cattle-feed in connection with the family milling business. The tower was struck by lightning, and the repair of this damage started what was to become a complete restoration. The cap frame was rebuilt as a circle, the trees being hauled out of the woods and sawn up by Mr Dallaway himself. The cap is of a domed type with a covering of sheet aluminium. To facilitate repair and repainting, a small gallery was built around the cap. A Sussex-type fan stage was constructed at the rear.

The windshaft came from Staplecross smock mill, which was pulled down in 1951. This was hoisted into position and a fine brake wheel built. A short upright shaft drives to a clasp-arm great spur wheel which meshes with wooden stone nuts. There is a third wooden pinion which takes the drive through a pair of wooden bevel gears to an oatcrusher.

The fan drives through an assortment of bevel gears to a specially designed skew gear which meshes with the rack, which fortunately still remained. A pair of common sails was erected and another pair followed during the 1970s. The difficulty of manufacturing the wooden gears and erecting the heavy parts is made the greater by its having been a single-handed effort. As this restoration may be considered the forerunner of all modern complete rebuilds, the use of proprietary gears in the fan mechanism is understandable. Most of the major restorations of this type have started with a complete mill which has very rotten timbers; this rebuild is made the more exceptional by having originated from an empty tower.

During 1958 two interesting restorations were started which, while undertaken by the Ministry of Works and a group including a county council, were of a type hitherto unknown; the complete restoration of windmills to working order.

Saxtead Green post mill, Suffolk (p.87), was completely dismantled, leaving only the trestle and roundhouse standing. Every timber which was not in perfect condition was replaced by the same type of timber as was used originally, and a new crown tree was fashioned from that of Wetheringsett mill which had recently been dismantled. The standard of workmanship was very high, and the mill is now in new condition. Assuming that the maintenance is of the same standard, there should be no need for major repairs to the mill body for many hundreds of years. A restoration of this magnitude was made possible by the mill being owned by the Ministry of Works, who had very deep pockets, and the fact that Mr Jesse Wightman, the millwright, lived locally and was able to supervise the entire work.

The windmill is in first-class working order but, sad to relate, it is not allowed to grind, and the sails are only fitted with enough shutters to allow them to idle when there is a good breeze.

Shipley smock mill, Sussex (p.110), was restored at about the same time as a memorial to the writer Hilaire Belloc. The work was undertaken by the millwrights

Burwell, Cambridgeshire. *Seen shortly after it last worked in the 1950s. Note the tarred tower and the cluster of supporting buildings around the base, all of which have since been changed.*

Punnetts Town, Sussex. *Seen during renovation. At this time Mr Dallaway had spent 23 years rebuilding the mill.*

E. Hole and Son, and was exceptional in that a decision was taken that the mill should be made actually to grind corn. Built in 1879, this is a very modern mill with much iron machinery, and was in fact in quite a reasonable state of repair. The stocks were replaced, and repairs carried out to the cant posts, sails, cap frame and boarding, as well as to minor items like the stage. The generally good condition of the mill is indicated by the fact that the bill came to only a little over £4,000. When it is considered that the mill was made to grind and that it had last been used in 1926, this was not expensive.

Mr Powell, the son of the last miller, used the mill a good deal after the restoration, and in fact ground sixty tons of grain during one winter. Since his untimely death some years ago a little grinding has been done, but only for demonstration purposes. The sails may be seen turning on most weekends during the summer, when the interior can be inspected for a small charge.

Wrawby post mill, Lincolnshire, was restored by a group of enthusiasts who rebuilt the mill completely after dismantling virtually the entire structure. Post mills are extremely rare in the North-east, which makes this restoration of great importance, for not only is the mill restored, but it is also in frequent use.

Another mill in constant use is that at Over in Cambridgeshire, which has been restored by its owner in his spare time. This was a single-handed piece of work which deserves great credit.

The windmill at Nutley in Sussex (p.122) is a small old post mill of considerable age which last worked during the 1920s. It stood with the battered remains of its spring sweeps until the owner of the estate upon which it stands had a set of bare sail frames erected in the early 1930s. The body was also underpinned in the breast as there was a damaged side girt. More work was carried out in the mid-1950s, which included the strengthening of some main timbers.

The end of 1969 saw the trestle decayed to such an extent that the post had dropped down from the crowntree and the entire weight was being taken by the underpinning. The two corner posts in the breast had almost rotted through and the breast beam which they supported was carrying the full weight of the sails.

An agreement was reached between a private group and the owner, and the tricky job of removing the sails without bringing about the destruction of the entire mill was accomplished. An appeal was launched and work proceeded with great speed. The owner did not wish the mill to be dismantled and rebuilt, which meant that the whole body had to be supported while many main timbers were replaced (p.123). A remarkable achievement was the remaking and replacing of the crosstrees and quarterbars. This difficult work was carried out at weekends during the winter months and was completed in a very short time.

A pleasing aspect of this restoration is that any timbers which are usable have been retained, and if the joint had become rotten a new end was spliced on. The final result is as near to the original state as possible, and yet the whole building is as good as new. When entering a mill like Saxtead Green there is an inevitable feeling that it is a new mill. This is not the case at Nutley, the reconstruction of which is an interesting attempt to combine the best of both worlds.

The trestle at Garboldisham Common mill, Norfolk was renewed shortly after that at Nutley, the work being undertaken by the millwrights Messrs Lennard and Pargeter. This was not an easy job, for the piers were quite high and leaning and the mill had moved off-centre, necessitating the tricky task of manoeuvring the entire structure some inches back to the centre. The mill is slowly being restored to working order, the fan turning the mill to wind again in the early 1990s.

THE RESTORATIONS

The last twenty years have not only seen an increase in the restoration, as opposed to repair, of windmills, but a considerable improvement in the standard aimed for and achieved. The ultimate purpose of the restoration has also tended to change, for whereas a static structure with skeleton fan and lifeless sails devoid of any shutters or striking gear was once regarded as success, the goal has moved through that of a mill that winds itself and has a scatter of shutters to enable idling on an open day, to one of full operation with flour for sale. The flour may be a bit rough, but the pleasure given to those who run the mill and try to teach themselves the art of flour milling on the open days during the summer, the visitors who pay to see and hear the windmill at work and those who merely pass by and see the sails turning, is proportionately far greater than the additional expense incurred in bringing the mill to life.

Ash, Kent. *Blown down in 1953. A very young Vincent Pargeter is seen standing amongst the wreckage near the ladder.*

I was once asked to carry out a survey on Clayton post mill by its owners, the district council. A millwright had told the relevant officials that it was impracticable to consider restoring the mill to working order. I strongly denied this, for I guessed that the millwright had made the error of judging the situation from his experience of other, less enlightened, owners. The answer was a phased restoration, starting with the basic structural problems and finishing with the item that every councillor's attention seems to focus upon – the sails. One side girt end had failed, causing the crowntree to tilt across the mill, the breast beam was weak and a fair amount of crude repair work was in evidence, but the mill was reasonably complete and a good candidate for full restoration. There were many leaks and I emphasised very strongly that these should be cured without delay, for the apparently innocuous drips of water were causing the demise of otherwise sound original timbers. There was one very serious leak where the roundhouse roof had been admitting rain for years on to a crosstree end. Remembering that Ash mill had been lost by just such a fault, while the owner and council procrastinated over the purchase, I felt that shock tactics were justified.

"If you do not instruct the millwright *at once* to put an iron strap on that", I said, pointing at it, "you will not have a windmill to restore". They did, and thanks to an enthusiastic band of amateur millwrights, this mill has been returned to working order.

There has been a logical progression from rebuilds like that at Saxtead Green where vast amounts of public money were spent to preserve an example of a post mill for future generations, to Nutley where the mill was made capable of work with some shutters in the sails, and onward to Clayton post mill which carries a full complement of shutters. These mills have been renovated primarily for public access and instruction. The final progression of this encouraging trend has been left to the private owner; Mr James Waterfield of Boston illustrating the case well.

Mr Waterfield ran the post mill that had been moved from Danzy Green to the Ashcroft Museum of Rural Life near Birmingham, before progressing to restore and run Bardwell tower mill. This was ultimately sold due to its limited size and output and to the difficulty of manoeuvring articulated lorries into the mill yard. The next project was at Boston (p.120). This five-sailed mill had stood with barren, shutterless sails for many years beside the Maude Foster drain in the centre of the town. The site was used for industrial purposes and was run-down and shabby. Mr Waterfield and his father renovated the mill and its surroundings with the result that the area now looks much as it did in the windmill's previous working days and is a major asset to an attractive part of the town. The output of this large mill was ultimately insufficient and Mr Waterfield has now leased Alford mill from the council, Mr Waterfield senior having joined his son in the business to run the mill at Boston while the younger generation works that at Alford.

This is the largest windmilling operation in England and one particularly remarkable aspect is that the considerable output is not of grist, but of flour, a part of the industry that died with the onset of the First World War.

The main body of stone-ground flour today is literally "whole" meal. That is to say that whereas wholemeal at one time indicated a flour for brown bread with the flakes of bran removed in a dresser, but otherwise unadulterated, the new green age consumer demands bran in large quantities. To this end meal is ground with as much of the bran cut up as possible and some millers are even using peak stones for the flour trade. What the old-time millers would have to say is probably best left to the imagination, for one hundred years ago bran and peak stones were definitely regarded as the province of horses and cattle.

That the flour was no less wholesome, I can vouch for, for Deans water mill in Sussex used to grind the wheat from local farms and distribute it through the owner's chain of healthfood shops. French stones were used and the result passed through a traditional bolter. The final product found its way into my parent's household and tasted very good indeed.

Mr Waterfield is adding this more traditional meal to his list of products and it is to be hoped that the business will flourish and its owner long continue to delight visitors with his selection of brightly coloured waistcoats and his sunflower-shaped umbrella.

Amongst the mills that grind seriously, that is to say where production varies from a few tons a year to help with the cost of maintenance to as large an output as the wind will produce, Swaffham Prior tower mill in Cambridgeshire and Sarre smock mill in Kent, come to mind.

Danzey Green Mill.
Shown at the Avoncxroft Museum, Worcestershire. A rebuilt post mill containing the post from another mill which had long been demolished. Note the narow midlands-type roundhouse with the quarter bar ends projecting through the wall.

Asterly, Shropshire. *As it stood in 1958 and, photographed by R Seabrook, as rebuilt. A remarkable achievement. This windmill will eventually return to work.*

Sarre mill (p.118) was rather different. Last worked by wind in 1920, the sails, fan and cap roof had gone, to be replaced with an unpleasant, but watertight corrugated iron covering. As is so often the case, most of the light woodwork had been removed and despite still containing its basic machinery, the mill was in a sad state. Fortunately it was purchased by Mr Hobbs, a skilled joiner, and he and his son set about a complete renovation. The intention was to repair the mill as near as possible to its appearance when last active and then return it to full work. This has been achieved and an interesting bonus has been the saving of a great deal of money previously spent on fuel for the gas engine that drove one pair of stones. Sarre mill is prominently placed both for wind and tourism and no doubt the turning sails have also attracted more customers for the flour.

It was gristing that saved the windmill from early extinction, but this trade has now suffered a serious decline. The replacement of the carthorse by the tractor, the reduction of stock on farms and the near monopoly held by vast companies that deliver twenty-ton loads of meal direct to farmers, the contents of each bag carefully blended with any required additives, have all contributed to this contraction. Mr Biggadike, who finally closed his business in the power-driven Moulton windmill, Lincolnshire, in 1994, said that there was a time when many country households kept a pig or chickens, or even a pony for use in a cart, but that now this trade has almost entirely vanished.

The loss of the grist trade is a shame, for the variety of grains stored in the heaps of sacks lent interest to the interior of a mill and each type smelt different, both in the bag and whilst being ground. There was also a variation in sound as the grain passed between the stones, maize producing a loud roaring noise, while wheat sang sweetly. I was pleased to see barley being ground at Over mill recently, for the sound and smell took me back to my childhood when that was what I usually saw being milled.

In recent times there have been some heroic rebuilds. In 1958 I visited Asterly mill, Shropshire. This was a stone-built tower mill with the remains of a cap frame and a few rotten timbers crossing the lower part of the interior. The owners were small farmers who knew little about the windmill, other than that it had not worked for a considerable time.

A few years ago Mr Peter Lewis bought it and commenced a complete rebuild. There was no windshaft or mechanism remaining, other than some segments of

the cast iron curb with upward facing rack. The tower was repaired where it had cracked, a new curb made and new rack segments cast. The cap frame was copied in the same massive timber sections as the original, the shape of the roof being calculated from old photographs of the mill and others in the general area. The Western part of England has a tradition of tower mills with wheel-and-chain luffing gear, but an old man could remember that there had once been "a propeller thing at the back", and that has been built and fitted. There were also patent sails and old photographs showed a stanchion for the brake lever on the left-hand side of the cap frame – proof that these rotated in a clockwise direction.

The massive windshaft is of timber and has an iron poll end cast from a pattern made by Mr Lewis himself. This was assembled into the cap frame on the ground and the whole hoisted onto the tower by a mobile crane, the bleak aspect of the tower on the skyline being transformed in a few minutes once again into a windmill.

May 1994 saw a set of sails erected, the whips and stocks being made from laminated timber, a useful compromise in an era when large section timber of the right sort is in short supply. Items built from laminated timber can be very strong, and old-fashioned wooden aircraft propellers were made in the same way, not due to a lack of suitable timber, but because they were much more resistant to the stresses imposed on them.

There are some parallels between Asterly and Punnetts Town. Both were landmark restorations of their time, both owners worked single-handed, both have had their timber sawn from the round by their owners, and the intention both times has been to make the mill work. Another similarity is that their owners have carried out the work with their own finances and without the intention of opening to the public.

Of course the standards of authenticity are different. Asterly has been restored with very careful attention to historical accuracy, whereas the work at Punnetts Town was carried out at a time when there was little concern for such refined attitudes. Indeed, one has the feeling that Mr Dallaway probably enjoyed adapting various bits and pieces of machinery to his purpose. Another variation is in the backgrounds of the restorers: Mr Dallaway being a miller and agricultural engineer, whereas Mr Lewis spends much of his time playing and teaching the violin.

The satisfaction of having converted trees into such an intricate machine is immense, and one has a vision of Mr Lewis watching his mill at work while the same hands that fashioned the heavy timbers and finely-shaped gear teeth fret and bow his violin on the fan stage.

The amount of work for one man in the rebuilding of a windmill may be judged from the figures for the sails at Asterly: two stocks, sawn to a taper and planed; four sails, the whips morticed with the correct weather and sawn and planed to a taper; 192 shutters to be framed up with mortices and tenons and covered with canvas; patterns to be made for the shutter cranks, both left- and right-handed for leading and trailing edges; patterns for shutter pivots and thimbles, and patterns for the spider and triangles of the striking gear. After the patterns have been made the foundry has to cast: 192 shutter cranks; 192 shutter pivots; 384 thimbles and the triangles and spider.

When all the castings have been returned, they have to be fettled to remove rough edges, drilled and countersunk for screws and attached to the shutter frames. Quite a task!

There is no substitute for the use of traditional tools that have evolved from empirical studies, but the addition of electric hand saws, for ripping and cutting tapers, band saws for finer cutting and for the forming of, say, shutter tenons, an electric plane and a morticing machine can speed up the work considerably, especially when one is involved in mass production of items like shutter frames. The availability of these machines at reasonable prices must have contributed quite substantially to the practicality of either a small group or a single individual taking on the task of full restoration. The modern mobile crane also has a part to play, for a cap can now be rebuilt with greater ease and safety on the ground and then hoisted into position, something that would surely have brought a smile to the faces of the original builders, for they had to assemble a cap piece by piece with no scaffolding at anything up to one hundred feet above the ground.

Ringwould, Kent. *The despoiled remains in the early 1960s. This mill is now well on the way to returning to work.*

The luxury of a crane has also been used lately to fit stocks and sails. This is easy, but really a waste of money, and there is a tendency for the people working on the sails to become pressurised by the mounting cost of any delay. E. Hole and Son have recently reverted to the old method of using a winch and cables where a couple of men are able to work unobtrusively and at their own speed to sort out any problems.

Remarkable as it may seem, the Asterly rebuild does not represent the only work of its kind, nor the ultimate level of windmill building that has been reached. The smock mill at Ringwould, Kent was devastated during the 1950s when a television company tore off the cap and removed the entire machinery and interior with the intention of using the mill as a relay station. Prior to this it had worked through the 1930s with two sails and had ended up with one sail, but otherwise complete, and would have been a certain candidate for renovation as a landmark. Unfortunately the television company had other ideas and what was left of the mill was adorned with grotesque aerials and wires, the edifice being illustrated in various newspapers as a clever new use for an old mill.

In the later 1980s, the company had a change of plan and the mill was advertised for sale at £25,000. I have always liked the old pictures of this mill and the site is both attractive and good for wind, so seriously considered making a purchase. There was, however, no house with it and Ringwould is a long way from where I normally live. Common sense reluctantly ruled and the mill was

Thrigby, Norfolk. *As rebuilt. The sails and machinery are not yet in place.*

purchased by Mr and Mrs Atkinson, who have started their own version of the Asterly rebuild. At the time of writing, the tower has been renovated and a new cap built and fitted. This carries the windshaft from Shiremark mill which was burnt down by vandals in the early 1970s. This is the third home for this shaft, for it is a post mill windshaft with squares for a brake and tail wheel, the centre for the wooden clasp arm brake wheel at Shiremark having been wedged on to the central section.

There were originally three pairs of stones fitted, driven from below, so the output from this windy position should be quite considerable.

Many year ago, before he was a millwright, Philip Lennard dismantled the post mill at Chinnor in Oxfordshire to save it from demolition. This was a very rare three crosstree and six quarter-bar mill and was one of only two such windmills remaining. The other stood

at Moreton in Essex and was in the care of the County Council. Appalling as it now seems, the council took the decision to demolish this important mill in 1964, leaving no mills of this type standing.

Fortunately, Mr Lennard had stored Chinnor mill in the hope that he would one day find a site where it could be re-erected. The mill has now changed hands and is being slowly reassembled at Chinnor, not on the original site, for that has been built over, but quite close to its first home. For many years this mill was stored in Essex, a ghost visiting the scene of the demise of its kinsman!

By way of restitution for their previous misdeeds, Essex County Council now has one of the most comprehensive schemes for the preservation of mills of any county and Mr Vincent Pargeter works full time to restore and maintain a growing portfolio of mills, including those at Aythorpe Roding, Mountnessing and Stock, which have been repaired to working order.

Extraordinary as it would have seemed when this book was first written, the history of the windmill has now evolved to an even further stage; complete new windmills are being built. The problem with being a windmill enthusiast is that there is a high possibility that one may live in a part of the country which is more or less devoid of windmills, or the mills one wants may be owned by other people who resolutely refuse to move elsewhere. Faced with such a problem, what does the true enthusiast do? He builds his own!

Some years ago Mr and Mrs Prior bought a house at Thrigby in Norfolk. In the garden was a roundhouse containing the trestle of a post mill that had been taken down a very long time before. The roundhouse inspired Mr Prior to

Leinthall Starkes, Herefordshire. *A new windmill and probably the only smock mill to be built in the county.*

recreate what had gone and this he did during the 1980s. The post had been cut off at the top of the roundhouse roof and the trestle was rather rotten, so the whole was replaced, the top clamping ring of the post being a discarded item from an oil rig which came Mr Prior's way due to his being a geologist in the oil industry. The mill is substantially built with heavy timbers and contains quite a number of parts from the collapsed Eye mill, Suffolk. The windshaft is an iron one from Tottenhill mill which was taken down in 1961 when very derelict. Someone had attempted to cut off the tail of the shaft, but a repair has been made with a steel sleeve and a new brake wheel fitted to the forward part to drive two pairs of stones side by side in the breast. These have yet to be installed, but the tentering gear is in place and one pair of stones has been purchased.

Originally Thrigby mill had two common and two patent sails and tailpole winding. In the interests of safety while its owner is away on business, the current

building has been altered somewhat, a ladder fantail being fitted which will eventually use the iron parts from Eye mill and a set of common sails is envisaged. The site is a good one for wind and pleasantly rural with views across the Broads to many pumping mills in various states of repair. It is also interesting that the parts of three lost mills have been brought together, both in preservation and in future work.

Thrigby mill is on the site of a previous windmill and could, with some stretching of the imagination, be regarded as a restoration, but Leinthall Starkes mill (p.145) is all new. Erected on some spare land that the owner happened to possess, this mill has been constructed by its owner and a friend who owns, and has restored, a watermill. The result is a large smock mill with patent sails and a fantail. I have not been inside, but am told that as yet there is no machinery and that a final decision on the internal arrangements has yet to be taken.

Apart from my own little post mill, built in 1959 (of which more later), Leinthall Starkes mill is the first new windmill to be built in England since Birdham pumping mill, Sussex, in the mid 1930s, and St Margarets Bay electricity generating mill in 1929. There are, however, more to come.

Mr Richard Seago has obtained planning consent to build a post mill at South Walsham in Norfolk and has acquired the post and samson head from the lost Topcroft post mill, also in Norfolk, with the intention of re-using these in his new mill. Away on the opposite side of England, Mr Lewis has been granted both planning permission and building regulations permission to erect a post mill on a fine site close to his tower mill at Asterly and is already laying in timber to season, while at Pease Pottage in Sussex, timber is being purchased and seasoned to make a copy of my own windmill.

The 1990s must surely be the epoch of the bureaucrat, and it is interesting that whereas it was thought necessary at Asterly to obtain planning consent to renovate the tower mill, which was already a substantial building, in other situations it has been felt either that the work was a repair and therefore did not require renewed permission, or that it was an agricultural building and was outside the normal planning procedures. Whichever is the correct interpretation of the law, it is to be hoped that the authorities will view applications with a benign eye and that prospective mill owners will not be forced to pay for needless structural engineer's calculations and will be obliged to conform to nothing more onerous than the traditional, and effective, methods of construction.

WINDMILLS LOST

Unfortunately the last couple of decades have not been without their negative side. The rise in living standards has caused increased pressure on potential development land in and around villages and several windmills have been engulfed by new housing.

There have been a couple of sad losses from the hurricane of 1987. To be outside in the greatest wind since 1703 was a stunning experience. I remember standing on my lawn at three-thirty in the morning and watching huge trees several feet thick swaying back and forth like tufts of grass in a stiff breeze. Branches were being torn off by the dozen, and the air, some fifteen miles inland, smelt of

Winchelsea, Sussex. *After the hurricane of October 1987.*

sea salt. Trees were lashing so wildly that a few even crashed over on the backswing as the gusts momentarily eased. Vincent Pargeter tells me that Mountnessing post mill was bucking so violently that he dared not raise the ladder to turn it closer to the eye of the wind.

That any windmill could survive such an onslaught without damage would seem good luck, but that Windmill Hill post mill should still be standing the next morning was nothing less than a miracle. This mill had never been restored or even properly repaired since it last worked in 1892, and with side girts completely rotted through and with the full force of the hurricane commencing on the side and moving round

147

to the tail, one can only really say that one is glad not to have been in it at the time!

Winchelsea post mill was not so fortunate. When I first went inside this mill in 1961 it was watertight and used as a hay store by the shepherd who looked after the sheep in the nearby fields. It was quite a large mill which had once driven two pairs of stones, head and tail, and had a third pair in the tail of the bin floor which had apparently been used for grinding beans. Most of the mechanism was complete, but, as is so often the case, the stone vats and furniture had gone, as had the windshaft which had had a wooden poll end and had carried two common and two spring sails.

This area of Sussex and Kent once had a number of post mills with roof mounted fantails. This and Icklesham on an adjacent hill were the only survivors, the proximity of the two mills being an added attraction. The fan had been dismantled, but the entire mechanism had been carefully stored in the roundhouse to await the attention of a future restorer.

The restorer never came. The mill was repaired in response to damage, but the work was carried out with such brutality that the remaining structure was devastated. Every piece of machinery was torn out, the roof was replaced with a crude structure that did not conform to the original shape, and virtually the whole of one side was renewed with a network of light steel faced with roughly hewn softwood to carry the boarding. The elegant matching brake and tail wheels were feared at the time to have been consigned to the bonfire, but a letter some time later from Mr Frank Gregory to the public body that owned it revealed that they had been sent into storage. He later visited the storage depot to find that no-one had heard of them. It is to be hoped that these important gears do still exist somewhere and that they have not been inadvertently destroyed.

The story of Winchelsea mill should be portrayed as an example of what not to do on two counts; firstly, what was once an original and relatively complete historic building was ruined through thoughtless repair, and secondly, the repairers clearly misunderstood the theories of post mill construction.

Post mills and the caps of smock and tower mills remain stable by the use of two forces; geometry and weight. It is a fact that the larger a structure, the smaller the proportion of surface area to volume. For this reason Windmill Hill mill will remain sitting firmly on its piers during a hurricane, whereas a twelve-inch high model in the garden will end up in the next village. Winchelsea mill had lost its weight through the removal of the contents and the heavy framing timbers, and it appears that this probably caused its demise.

An examination of the remains a few days after the collapse (p.147) led me to the impression that the hurricane, bearing full force on the side of the mill, had overturned the trestle. It is also possible that the post cantilevered up against two quarterbars, allowing the others to drop clear of their mortices and the horns of the post to rise free from the crosstrees. Whatever the exact cause, the trestle ended up in parts, but without apparent structural failure.

The hurricane started from the south and gradually changed direction to finish blowing from the west, the fury travelling diagonally across Southern England to make its exit into the North Sea via East Anglia. Clayton post mill was almost burnt down due to the brake wheel somehow freeing itself from its chocks and the rim being set on fire as the sails started off with the brake hard on. Only an heroic effort by two custodians, who were reached before the telephone lines were finally destroyed, and who managed to put water on the fire and throw ashes on to the brake rim to improve the grip, saved the mill, which also suffered the failure of the original ladder-hinges and the severance of the ladder from the mill body, the disaster of a tail wind being prevented by the tailpole fantail holding the mill from swinging free.

Sails were broken off Rolvenden and Argos Hill mills, the last running at normal working speed against the brake until a stock sheared, the flying sails causing much damage, but saving the mill from fire. At Nutley the leverage against the post was so great that two horns were broken from the post and the entire structure keeled over to be somehow saved by the ladder jamming against the tailpole.

At Bardwell a fan gear came out of mesh and the fully working mill was tailwinded, the brute force of the gale snapping the rear box of the poll end from the neck of the windshaft and the sails crashing into the mill yard. Bardwell mill survived and a new windshaft has been cast, but Syleham (p.150) post mill was not so lucky. I saw this mill during the 1950s when it was still in working order. A tailwinding episode in 1947 had left it with only two sails, but the side girts had been strengthened and it was complete and quite straight, although the breast corner posts had been reduced in thickness in places by rot. The sails were ultimately stripped of their shutters and left diagonally (not a good position with two sails as it can impart a yawing motion to the structure in a strong wind and, as has been said earlier, is more of a strain on the stock than the vertical position), the owner continuing a milling business with a pair of engine-driven stones in the roundhouse. Little more was done to the mill until the hurricane hit and the corner post failed on the side opposite the uppermost sail, causing the bin floor and windshaft to collapse to the ground. Sadly, that is how the mill remains, a complete and restorable mill that is slowly rotting away.

Nutley, Sussex. *After restoration.*

CANDIDATES FOR RESTORATION

The late Mr Jesse Wightman once told me that now that Swilland mill had gone, Friston was the finest remaining post mill. Swilland must have been quite wonderful, for Friston is a magnificent windmill. There were originally three pairs of stones, all driven indirectly, the tail pair offset to the left. These were regrettably removed when the business was sold, but otherwise the building is in very sound and original condition, the full-length side girts being cambered upwards at the

Syleham, Suffolk.
Shown here shortly after stopping work for good in the 1950s.

tail and, unusually nowadays, have never been repaired or strengthened. During the 1970s much repair work was carried out to the breast, and the mill is slowly being renovated to full working order. Mr Piers Hartley, the owner, is adamant that all new work shall be completely authentic and that nothing shall be done to despoil the original parts.

The sails were just under nine feet in width and seventy-five feet in span and produced sufficient power to drive all the equipment in a good wind; that is to say, three pairs of stones, an oat crusher, jog scry and flour dresser. The roof ridge is approaching fifty-five feet in height, making this the tallest post mill in England. The intention is that it will be a proper working mill and there are many people who can barely wait to see such a fine mill grinding again.

Windmill Hill mill has just been rescued from the verge of collapse. This is the second-tallest post mill at forty-nine feet to the ridge. The four patent sails were removed in 1892 and all future grinding carried out by engine-driven stones in the roundhouse. One wonders whether the miller had become nervous, for not only did wind operation cease early, but a sail governor had been fitted to control the speed of the sails, the post had been strengthened with iron strips coachscrewed into the neck where it passed through the collar, the windshaft was strengthened with timber clamps, heavy sag irons (iron bracing bars) had been fitted at either end of the crowntree to hold up the four corners, and there is evidence to show that iron plates had been bolted to the inner face of each side girt. The last have been removed at some time, an impossible task had the side girts failed before removal. The side girts are rather light for so large a mill, at fifteen and a half by nine inches, but the weight was not as great as Friston, for only two pairs of head and tail stones were fitted.

There are a number of interesting features, including a cambered lower crosstree and the indent of a jack head on the underside of each crosstree, a legacy of the mill having been raised to a two-storey roundhouse. The most striking feature is the originality, for even the original leather driving belts are in place, after more than a hundred years of idleness. It also has the largest surviving body at twenty-one feet two and a half inches long by twelve feet four and a half inches wide.

The side girts have rotted through, the crowntree ends are crumbling away and the structure has dropped, causing a massive hump in the spout floor, but it has recently been supported by an iron frame and made watertight. All that is now needed is the money and enthusiasm to restore it to working order.

Moulton mill, Lincolnshire is the tallest windmill in England. It lost its windshaft and sails one hundred years ago, but the cap frame, most of the fan gears and the machinery are all complete. At this precise moment, it even feels like a working windmill, for Mr Biggadike has only just closed his business. This is a Grade One listed building which must increase the availability of grants. What is now required is a Lincolnshire-based enthusiast to come forward to restore it as a working mill and preserve its present atmosphere.

There are other mills with machinery and no cap. Chislet in Kent and Great Welnetham in Suffolk come to mind, plus, of course, the two windmills at Drinkstone, the post mill complete with four sails and the smock mill without machinery or windshaft, but still displaying the old beehive-type Suffolk cap.

Strange as it may seem, with almost-complete windmills waiting to be restored, there are mills which have almost ceased to exist in the early stages of rejuvenation. All that remains of the five-sailed smock mill at Sandhurst, Kent, is the two storey brick base, but this has been purchased with the intention of a rebuild; the same is rumoured to apply to the base and cut-down wooden tower of Baldslow mill, Hastings. A different situation applies to Washington smock mill, Sussex (p.155), a mill that was thoroughly ruined many years ago when it was part-submerged into a house. The site is like an isthmus projecting into a sandpit and has finally been bought by the mining company. The house will be demolished, but the sound wooden tower is to be found a new home. The first reaction is that it could be placed on an existing base, like that at Billingshurst a few miles away, but then neither mill would be quite authentic to its original state.

Apart from the utilisation of old mill parts in rebuilds, there is also a move to assemble machinery from lost or house-converted mills into a display. Both Gayton and South Ockenden, Essex, are currently having their remaining parts erected within another building.

Above: **Ringmer,
Sussex.** *After the collapse
of June 1925.
Negotiations for its
preservation were in
hand at the time, but
delays caused the loss of
this picturesque and
prominent mill. Mr
Geoffrey Rowland, a
local farmer's son, told
me that as a boy he and
his brothers walked
across the downs to the
mill and gained entry.
One of them raised the
brake and the sails "just
whipped round", after
which they ran away at
full speed, abandoning
the derelict mill to its
fate. One wonders
whether this hastened the
final collapse.*

Right: **Outwood,
Surrey.** *The smock mill
after being blown down
in 1961.*

Left: **Crowborough, Sussex.** *All that remained of the post mill in 1961 after it had been set on fire by an incendiary bomb during World War II.*

Below: **Shiremark, Surrey.** *An old mill with much wooden machinery. Burnt down by vandals during the early 1970s. The windshaft has now been installed in Ringwould mill, Kent and will once again be put to work.*

Below: **Hawkinge, Kent.** *Blown down in 1963.*

CHAPTER 14

Working a Windmill Today

By the 1970s there was only a small handful of windmills which were still used in conjunction with a milling business. Those at North Leverton, Nottinghamshire, Pakenham in Suffolk (p.34) and Stelling Minnis in Kent (p.28) were still the mainstay of their owners' businesses. That at Drinkstone (p.33) was an adjunct to the owner's business and was really run more for pleasure than commerce. The same applied to Alford in Lincolnshire (p.119) where the tower mill was owned by a firm from a nearby village who ran it occasionally. The majority of the remainder were used only for demonstration to the public, two of the exceptions being Punnetts Town (p.136) and Over (p.98).

Windmills were no longer a commercial proposition, and behind every working mill there was an enthusiastic owner. Without these people there would have been no windmills working in this country. Farmers were able to buy their animal

Washington, Sussex. *Seen in its working days.* Old postcard.

North Leverton, Nottinghamshire. *One of only two windmills to have never ceased work.*

155

Drinkstone, Suffolk.
In its working days.

feeds from big milling companies which delivered ten or twenty tons at a time from as far away as forty or more miles. Such companies were often able to supply feed cheaper than the local miller, and with farming itself under severe economic pressure, inevitably trade drifted away. Even cattle or pig food has special additives nowadays, which can often only be contained economically in feeds produced in vast bulk. Many small millers were agents for these large companies, but nonetheless were frequently closing their doors for good.

A problem that began to face windmillers was that of disposal of the finished product, although there was some scope where specialist feeds were concerned. Very large firms are usually reluctant to produce any special or small batches and this has reacted in the small miller's favour.

THE STONES

Stone dressing was a problem also, for those who were really skilled were becoming few indeed. Since the death of Mr Powell, the stones at Shipley had not been dressed, and it was wondered who would do this when it was needed. This problem must face most groups of enthusiasts today when they decide to grind with their newly restored mill, but fortunately there are a number of partly or fully self-taught dressers who will travel to any part of the country for a reasonable fee. The old itinerant stone dresser of legend who trudged the country lanes has re-equipped himself for the modern age with a car, an angle grinder or Kango Hammer and, above all, a bag of traditional mill bills.

The problem of replacing worn-out stones is, as yet, not great, for there are hundreds of stones throughout the country which remain from demolished mills of all types. Stones do not wear very quickly anyway, and should easily last for a minimum of ten years, even in constant use.

To the problems of wear and of dressing there is one simple remedy, namely composition stones. These are often one-piece and are composed of carborundum or other very hard chippings mixed with cement. The surface is very rough and the fine stitching is not required, leaving only the furrows to be deepened and the surface levelled when the stones are lifted. Since they are composed of extremely hard chippings, dressing is only very infrequently required.

A small milling firm which owned two water mills and a one-time steam mill used a most interesting system. An ordinary millstone was turned face up and fitted with an extra iron band around the circumference. This was left a few inches proud and a cylindrical piece of tin was fitted in the eye, this also being left a few inches proud. A mixture of cement powder and hard chippings was produced to which a quantity of spirits of salt was added. After thorough stirring the resultant cement was spread carefully over the surface of the stone. The stone was left in this condition until the cement was absolutely dry, when the furrows were marked out and the surface levelled where necessary. The iron band was then punched down below the level of the stone face.

To cut the furrows and to carry out all dressing operations, a Kango Hammer was used. This is best described as an industrial drill which, while driven by electricity, operates on the principle of a pneumatic road-drill. A number of different bits are provided, and in skilled hands the tool can be used to great advantage. A Kango Hammer would certainly appear to be the answer to many a miller's dressing problems.

When grinding animal feed, the desire is to cut up as much of the bran as possible, whereas flour production for purposes other than the health food trade, where entirely whole meal is required, needs the bran in larger flakes. For this reason a composition stone of the type described above is not really suitable for traditional flour milling. However, traditional millstones are still made and no doubt their manufacturers will experience an unexpected increase in trade.

Repairs

Minor repairs are usually carried out by the miller himself. These normally include repainting, which used to be undertaken every three years or so, although nowadays there is frequently a longer gap. When painting a white post mill, like Keymer, Sussex, about three hundred weight of best lead paint was required. The mill body was painted from a cradle which was suspended by ropes passed over the mill roof and down to the ground on the far side. The cradle was entered either by a ladder or from a window.

Tar was frequently used to preserve the boarding and was very useful, although very messy to apply. It does have the disadvantage of having to be heated before application, but is excellent in its sealing properties and probably well repays its use. Many Kentish smock mills were tarred.

The Working Mill

Those who have worked a windmill will agree that it is a fascinating experience, and perhaps even those who have not had the pleasure of having the mill under their own control, but have visited working mills, will know something of this feeling. It is not surprising, therefore, that despite the problems of maintenance and the cost of upkeep, people strive to work windmills. People sail boats on the sea for pleasure, and there is certainly a great affinity between the two machines, so why not sail the ship of the land?

Naturally the greatest similarity is between an old post mill and a small sailing-boat, for the post mill becomes alive when in motion, and if the joints are rather worn the whole mill shakes and rolls when running fast in a stiff breeze. A tower mill is a far more reserved and stately affair, for when inside there is no apparent sensation of movement in the tower, and only the rumble of the runner stone, the faint clacking of the shoe and the rattle of the sack-hoist give any clue that the mill is at work.

Friston, Suffolk. *Here they climbed the ladder on the right.*

Moulton, Lincolnshire. *Here the handrail was on the left.*

As you enter a Lincolnshire-type tower mill the immediate sensation is one of warm dustiness, for there is a thin film of flour dust on most surfaces. Sacks are stacked against the walls, some full of grain waiting to be ground and others containing meal ready for despatch to the various local farms. To one side a broad ladder gives access to the floor above. The treads are deeply worn with the passage of hundreds of pairs of feet. A rope helps the visitor to steady himself as he climbs to the next floor.

This is the spout floor, and three bins stand together in the centre of the floor with wooden spouts descending to them from the floor above. Dust is in the air, for the miller is grinding barley which is always rather dusty. To try to reduce this he has left one of the two loading doors open, and this also helps to make the floor much lighter than the one below. There are always two loading doors in order to facilitate the loading of wagons or lorries, whichever way the sails are facing. The bins are highly polished by the friction of centuries of sacks, and into one a steady flow of barley meal is pouring. When handled this has a sweet smell and a yellow tinge. The miller is feeling the meal between his thumb and fingers and is adjusting a large wing-nut on the tentering gear above his head. In the ceiling the lower surfaces of the bed stones are visible, as are the governors driven from the stone-spindle.

The next floor up is the stone floor with one pair of stones rumbling beneath a gently rising dust cloud. The shoe is tapping away beneath the hopper, in which

Clayton, Sussex.
Internal view of the cap.

Left: **Windmill Hill, Sussex.** *Before work ceased in 1892, many people used this step to the bin floor.*

Clayton, Sussex.
External view of the cap.

the grain is observed to be constantly on the move as it flows out of the almost submerged end of the spout from the bins on the floor above. The great spur wheel is revolving overhead, and one stone nut is in gear while the others are leaning back on their quants in the disengaged position. The wooden teeth are well greased, and there is hardly any sound as they mesh with the iron stone nut. Through one window the backs of the white-painted sails can be seen flashing past.

The bin floor is quite small, for the tower has tapered considerably and almost the entire area is taken up by the bins. There is just room to stand beside the sack-trap and notice the shining sack-chain disappearing down through the much-worn holes to the floors below. The iron upright shaft is revolving slowly in the centre.

Another ladder leads to the dust floor which is even smaller than the last, and contains little besides the upright shaft and wallower with the sack-hoist ready for engagement with its lower side. Overhead the cap rises, with the brake wheel and windshaft turning slowly. Again there is little noise from the meshing of the wooden brake wheel teeth with those of the cast-iron wallower.

The wind is whistling around the cap, and there is quite a draught caused by the wind coming up under the petticoat (the name given to the ring of boards around the base of the cap). The wind can be heard in the sails, and when a heavy

Woolpit, Suffolk. *A very rare sight today, one windmill seen from another – Woolpit from the roof of Drinkstone mill. Even as late as 1953 there was enough trade to support independent businesses half a mile apart.*

gust strikes them the whole cap vibrates. A narrow portable ladder gives access into the cap itself, and when this is climbed the motion of the mill is at once apparent. The door to the fan stage is open and allows the only light to penetrate, for there are no windows on the dust floor, and the fan gears can be seen engaging with the thickly greased curb. A tub of grease for lubricating these and the neck and tail bearings is resting on the cap timbers. Beside them there is a large oil-can for oiling the fan bearings.

Stepping over the curb, it is possible to go out onto the small fan stage. This can be felt moving with the motion of the sails, and becomes even less steady when the fan suddenly starts to turn the cap. A ladder climbs towards one of the cross-braces of the fly posts from which the hand-rail of either fly post may be reached. To the visitor the prospect of climbing up the wooden blocks of the fly post is distinctly uninviting, for the wind can now be felt tugging at him as he climbs the short ladder and emerges into the air-flow. Turning to face the wind, the patent sails are seen turning on the far side of the beautiful ogee-shaped cap. As each reaches its zenith the air-flow is momentarily cut off from the observer, to resume as the sail rattles its way earthwards.

From a spot such as this sixty years ago, it might be possible to see as many as forty other windmills, all turning busily in the wind. Today, you may be fortunate to glimpse one empty tower on the skyline. Not only have the windmills gone, but so have the men who worked them, and in these days it is as much a privilege to meet an old miller who started work in Edwardian times as it is to stand on the fan stage of a truly working windmill.

WORKING A WINDMILL IN THE 1990S

It is not stretching credibility too far to say that it would have been feasible to stand on the upper floor of a windmill and look down upon the source of virtually every part. Timber from the local woods, brick from a nearby brickyard, iron smelted in the valley and forged in the village forge, stone for the roundhouse from a quarry a mile or two away, and even the millstones could come from the distant hills.

Today, most things that we handle or have contact with have emanated from some distant factory within which a mysterious process using multi-million pound machinery extrudes, treats or forms some simple or complex object. We use it or switch it on, but know that when it breaks, which it often does quite quickly, we will be unable to replace it with the effort of our own hands. Equally, we are aware that should the magical supply of electricity cease to travel down the wires or fuel no longer be available for driving our cars or heating our modern houses, many of the factory-made items would be useless.

There is a great satisfaction to be derived from bending iron in one's own forge or creating practical wooden objects. There is also satisfaction in seeing English grain pass through the millstones and emerge as flour. Climb up once again to the top of the windmill. We can see or imagine all the local places from where its parts were derived and all around are fields of grain. The wheat is cut and eventually finds its way to the windmill where it is turned into flour by grace of one of life's few remaining free sources of power – air.

It must surely be the windmill's unity with its district that causes it to add to, rather than detract from, the landscape. To the dedicated enthusiast, its attractions are multi-faceted, but to the less committed its creation from natural resources, its grace in action, its relative quietness in use and its utterly pollution-free conversion of an endlessly renewable power source, must rank it high on the list of acceptable machinery. There is an additional aspect to the above; while the windmill is going about its business, it is producing a wholesome product that is not only one of the basics of life, but also more than acceptable to even the most faddish vegetarian of the new "green" epoch.

It has been suggested that now that the computer has taken so much employment from the armies of clerical workers, and that factories and assembly lines are capable of being controlled by a few employees, people will have to accept a simpler way of life and that there will be a growth in one or two-man businesses. Fear of pollution may dictate that work will take place near where a person lives, to avoid travelling and the small town or village community could re-emerge.

Should this prove to be correct, the windmiller is ideally placed, for he not only produces a worthwhile product, but can also provide a service for the tourist and leisure industry.

The shelves of most bakeries and supermarkets contain stone-ground flour or products made therefrom. Much is ground using electric motors, but a fair quantity utilises the power of wind or water. There is a move in the labyrinths of the European Union to insist that member countries should produce a certain percentage of national power from renewable power sources. If such an idea fired the imagination of the public in the same way as the recycled paper lobby has done, and supermarkets labelled their stone-ground flour as having been produced by renewable, pollution-free power, then the future of the windmiller would be assured. One additional refinement could be that while the windmill supplied local bakeries direct, the main bulk of its production could be sold to a larger wholesaler who would supply the supermarkets. This would assist with quality control and even out supplies in addition to reducing competition.

It is typical of the lot of the human being that there are some very keen wind-mill enthusiasts who would wish for nothing better than to be a full-time windmiller, but who do not have the finances to buy or restore a mill, whereas those with the funds are unable to dedicate the time to milling. The answer in this case could be the granting of a licence to occupy and run a business from the windmill, which would enable a windmill to be in full-time work which might otherwise run only at weekends.

Framsden, Suffolk. *Before renovation this mill was owned by the same family as nearby Debenham tower mill.*

Kirton-in-Lindsey, Lincolnshire. *Fully restored to work. Here shown grinding, September 1993.*

CHAPTER 15

Broadhill Post Mill, Sussex

To write about my own windmill seems more than a little self-indulgent. This is not, however, the view held by some other enthusiasts who point out that this mill has its place in the history of the windmill and that as I know more about it than any other individual, I should be the one to write about it. To those who take the first view, may I apologise.

In 1958 I was a child who needed a windmill. As the nearby Keymer post mill was owned by the Sussex Archaeological Society, it was out of my reach, so I decided to build my own. Fortunately my parents believed in supplying materials for educational purposes and followed my argument that timber to build a post mill some fifteen feet high came within this category. The mill was duly constructed with a traditional design, but with nailed joints. At first there were four common sails and tailpole winding, but these were later altered to two commons and two spring sails with a ladder fantail. The gears and shafting for the fan were provided by E. Hole and Son and the iron wheels were salvaged from an old chicken house.

The mill worked well, for it was on the same ridge as the other Keymer mill, with an open aspect to Crowborough in the eastern sector, although the main south-westerly aspect was marred by a bank of trees. The machinery consisted of a small Bentall plate mill which was driven by belt from the windshaft.

During 1959 I decided to build a more authentic mill. At first I had a smock mill in mind, but the problems of sawing the curb sections by hand and the necessity of producing a properly geared brakewheel and wallower dissuaded me and I decided on a post mill.

I cut an ash tree for the post in one of our woods about a quarter of a mile away, and the windshaft came from another ash tree about half a mile distant. These were trimmed to size with an old-fashioned draw knife in part of a large garden shed and left to season while the other timbers were fashioned. Finances were restricted (the construction of *two* windmills was stretching the educational theory rather far) and softwood had to be used for most of the construction. This was perfectly adequate, but much more prone to decay than the usual hardwoods used in windmill framing.

The post was very heavy and was raised by a worm and chain gear suspended from home-made sheerlegs on a rather damp autumn day. To my great relief the quarterbars dropped nicely into their mortices and when I lowered the post, the trestle locked solid with seemingly even loading on each of the brick piers. The crowntree was hoisted later the same day and fitted easily onto the pintle.

The framing of the mill body was morticed and tenoned in the traditional manner, although I resisted cutting into the side girts at the maximum area of stress and used angle brackets at the point of contact with the crowntree rather than the more usual concealed dovetail.

A few days later the crowntree ends were roped down to a crosstree and the

Broadhill, Sussex. *As it is today on its new site. As seen, it runs two pairs of stones side by side in the breast.*

165

Broadhill. *The second mill being assembled from parts already made in the shed. Note the sheer legs used to lift the post.*

side frames lifted by hand while a friend fitted the tie beams in the breast and tail. This task was not easy and I suspect that the most likely method used by the old millwrights would have been that of swinging the end frames onto the side timbers, rather than the reverse.

When the framing and studding was all secure, a block and tackle were used to hoist the windshaft which was initially arranged to drive a nineteenth century oat kibbler by belt, a Bentall plate mill being added in the tail later. The end of the windshaft was morticed to form a three-way poll end and six single-shuttered spring sails were fitted

At first tailpole winding was used, but later I transferred the fantail from the other mill, converting it to a tailpole attachment as I felt this to be more traditional to the area.

The mill proved to be very powerful and the sails rather fast, possibly due to an optical illusion when so many sails were flashing past the side of the mill, or the low gearing of the machinery drive. The weather of the sail bars was acute at the heel, but shallow at the tip and this may also have contributed to the speed once running. The overall height was about twenty-seven feet and the sails two feet wide, so with six sails there was quite a sail area.

At this time I did not know about the ratio of the surface area to density changing with size and this proved to be fatal for the first mill, which was blown down during a very heavy storm in the early 1960s. The six-sailed mill remained unmoved despite being tailwinded due to the failure of the ladder hinges as happened at Clayton during the hurricane. This mill is very heavy and its stability demonstrates the margin of safety that must be present in a full-sized post mill.

By 1964 the poll end was showing signs of rot, and split during a severe gale. I decided that four sails were rather more elegant and E. Hole and Son welded up an iron poll end with a cylindrical mounting sleeve to fit the existing windshaft. The fitting of this coincided with a move to a house several miles away and I decided not to re-fit the sails for the time being. Eventually I came to the conclusion that a pair of common sails left vertically would be unlikely to cause damage and the mill last worked with these in 1972.

In 1989 I was living about nine miles away and decided that the time had come to move the windmill. It had been kept watertight, but had suffered from cattle entering the enclosure and breaking one of the sails, and vandals who did considerable damage to the boarding. The hurricane had caused further damage to the boarding a few years later, the mill surviving well despite a weakened side girt.

The problem of how I would eventually move the mill had occupied my mind for some years and I eventually hit on the idea of using an earth moving machine. The loading bucket was drilled to receive two girders which were bolted into position like the forks of a fork-lift truck. The side girt was strengthened and the tailpole and remaining stock removed, together with boarding from both sides of the body to allow entry of the forks below the side girts.

The day of removal came and the machine began to take the weight of the mill body. It creaked and swayed and then rose clear of the pintle. I had already dismantled the wooden roundhouse and unfastened the bands from the post. The trestle was taken apart and the mill raised enough to bring the post down through the collar, allowing the driver to lower the mill body onto a heavy trailer that was reversed beneath the suspended structure.

When all was securely roped into place we tried moving the trailer. It swayed dangerously, for the centre of gravity was very high. After a debate as to whether or not the whole equipe would turn over in the middle of Burgess Hill, I took down the windshaft, brake wheel and kibbler and placed them on the spout floor. The journey was accomplished without mishap. although the neck bearing was somehow dislodged by trees and lost.

After a careful examination, I decided to replace any timbers that were showing signs of decay. The trestle was in a particularly bad state and this was renewed in sweet chestnut, together with both side girts, the windshaft and various other structural timbers. The feet of the rafters were rotten and I took the opportunity to re-make these in a curved form which I would have preferred when the mill was first built had it not involved greatly increased use of timber and a great deal of hard work with a bow saw.

The new piers were built and the trestle placed in position, the ends of the crosstrees being held down with clamping bolts in readiness for any future hurricanes. Eventually all was ready and the machine returned to replace the body on the post. The sheers and collar were already in place, together with their mounting bolts and nuts. The end of one lower side girt was rotten, so I replaced this with a longer section spliced to the original. The flooring was left out, together with the weather boards from the lower sides. The new section of lower side girt was removed at the last minute and the mill body swung into position. The driver of the machine showed his considerable skill by aligning the socket with the pintle in a singe manoeuvre and in moments the work was complete. I bolted up the sheers and the lower side girt section, the machine withdrew its forks and there was the windmill standing on a nice new mound some nine miles from its original home.

The first brake wheel had been designed for braking purposes only, for I did not possess the expertise to make proper wooden gears. Rather than re-fit this, I decided to upgrade the machinery as I would have wished when the mill was first built. To this end a new brake wheel was made with forty-six wooden teeth meshing with a fourteen-tooth wallower. To start with the upright shaft drove the plate mill through a temporary trundle gear made one afternoon, the kibbler being hoisted into the spout floor to provide ballast.

Rather than face the problem of irregularities in the track straining the tailpole or mill, I decided to use a Suffolk-type fan, new bearings and a new vertical driving shaft provided by E. Hole and Son. This works very well indeed and was thoroughly tested for strength a week after fitting when the near hurricane-force wind of January 1990 hit the area.

The mill now carries a pair of common sails and a pair of spring sails, the spring sails being mounted on the outer stock in the traditional manner in order to avoid the open shutters fouling the mill body. The common sails vary from five degrees to twenty-four degrees, while the spring sails have a weather of seven to twenty-five degrees. The spring sails are particularly pleasant to work with as they start better, but are not as fast as the common sails. A small mill is rather susceptible to variations of wind speed and a full set of commons would require constant attention when the mill was running. The present arrangement is good, but there is a nagging temptation to make a second pair of spring sails, although this would require equal length shutters on both the leading and trailing edges in order to bring the shutters clear of the mill. Four spring sails would certainly make working easier in a strong and squally wind.

When I was sixteen I made some millstones from a pair of hard Portland Stone steddle stones which had once been used to support a granary. They were never fitted due to the problems of gearing and the cost of having various iron parts made. These were dressed for direct drive, but I required the reverse direction due to the use of an upright shaft. The removal of the old dressing and levelling of the surface took a great deal longer than its original installation and proved one thing quite clearly – there is no substitute for an old-fashioned mill bill.

These stones were re-dressed and assembled on a frame in my shed, various ironwork being bent to shape in my own forge and the mace being laboriously sawn, drilled and filed by hand. It was with great satisfaction that I poured some

grain into the eye and rotated the runner to find flour emerging at the skirt. When all the stone furniture had been made and a great spur wheel and stone nut manufactured, the whole was installed in the right-hand side of the mill breast, transfer and reassembly taking little more than a day.

There was no wind for several days, but I tested the work by turning the sails by hand and waited. At last a breeze came and the stones came to life, the sight and sound being authentic and very pleasing.

After using the mill like this for a while, I had a second pair of stones made from granite, delivery taking some months and the cost being rather high. These I use for grist, the barley making a characteristic sound as the hard grain passes between the faces before cascading down the chute to the bin.

Broadhill. *The second mill is seen during erection.*

Both pairs of stones are controlled by a single pair of governors, but there is a problem in that at speeds above one hundred revolutions per minute there is a tendency for the runner to rise on the grain and the meal to coarsen. Of course, the shoe also increases its feed as the speed rises and the grist stones now have a system similar to that at Silver Hill mill (p.70) where a wooden steelyard carries the twistpeg and this reduces the angle of the shoe as the governors rise. This evens out the problem of coarseness, although the optimum setting has the risk of the stones running too dry for a few revolutions as the speed falls. The real problem is that the stones are too light to hold down above one hundred revolutions per minute and the cure the simple one of setting the sails to run at speeds not exceeding about twenty revolutions per minute.

Not far away from where I live, there is a small timber yard and Mr Symes, the owner, is more than helpful when it comes to finding suitable wood for interesting applications. From this source came sweet chestnut as an unusual water-resistant substitute for oak, various types of cedar and pine for boarding, douglas fir, cyprus, ash and even apple. Now that so much elm has been destroyed by Dutch Elm Disease, this timber is hard to find, but ash is a good substitute for it is hard and very resistant to splitting. For this reason all but one gear are made from this timber, the exception being the wallower which is of elm. Some of the gear teeth are also of ash as there was no seasoned apple available at the time. I now have a supply and this will eventually be used as a replacement. Apple is hard and resistant to splitting and works particulary well, it being possible to pare a gear tooth across the face without risk of splitting the far edge.

I suppose the manufacture of a wooden gear is the most taxing task the millwright has to face. Beside gear making, the morticing of a sail whip is simple. The challenge, however, is more than worthwhile, for to have converted a tree into a piece of machinery with accurately spaced teeth of a correct profile that is quiet in work and strong enough to drive heavy machinery is a very rewarding experience indeed. As an entirely self-taught woodworker, my observation is that anything can be done so long as one thinks very carefully about what is required, uses traditional methods, calculates with care and never cuts anything without re-checking the measurements.

The present site of the windmill is potentially good, for it is over 300 feet above sea level and to the south the terrain is open to the South Downs some ten miles away. The problem, though, is trees. These are prominent in all directions and cause little trouble in winter, but much difficulty when in full leaf. The problem is not a direct one, for the mill looks over those to the south, but an indirect one; the wind hits a neighbour's bank of sycamore trees and veers to one side which causes the fan to drive the mill a few degrees out of the eye of the wind. The result is most frustrating, for the mill works well in light breezes, but is often unable to take advantage of those on a pleasant summer day.

Old millers have been quoted many times as wishing that they could once again be working their windmills when a nice wind blew. I know that during the period of idleness of my windmill, the urge quite frequently gripped me and that now I only have to hear the early morning wind in the trees to spring out of bed and climb the rise above my house to set the sails turning, hear the rumble of the stones and feel the swaying of the floor beneath my feet.

Broadhill, Keymer, Sussex. *The mill at work with six sails.*

170

CHAPTER 16

The Future

William Coles-Finch photographed many Kentish windmills in the early days of their decline and from these records there came one of the finest windmill books to be published. Robert Thurston Hopkins, an author of more than eighty books, was also actively interested before the First World War. Both must have been told many technical details of windmilling and of the erection of windmills. Unfortunately, if either knew the secret of the method of building a post or smock mill, neither recorded it and it is interesting that Wetheringsett mill was built a mere fifty-one years before the publication of W. Coles-Finch's book and only forty-eight years had elapsed since the construction of Swingfield smock mill, Kent. For that matter, the last tower mill had been built forty-one years earlier and St Margaret's Bay generating smock mill only four years before.

There are many people around who have within their memories first-hand stories and information recounted to them by millers and millwrights who worked in the last days of traditional windmilling. This, however trivial it may seem, should be recorded, for if it is not, it will be lost as surely as the secret of Wetheringsett mill has been lost.

This book was first written at a time when the last few working windmills were finally coming to a halt and the remaining traditional windmillers reaching the end of their working lives. The trend was one of retirement rather than complete loss, but there was an air of stillness, of looking back.

The intervening years have reversed this situation and despite the hardness of the present financial times, there is a feeling of hope for the future of the windmill. The nadir of the working windmill seems to have passed with only North Leverton and Alford making the transition from decline to renewed production without a break in their active lives. The outlook at the present time is not one of stillness, but of activity.

Parham, Suffolk. *The miller and staff with two loads of meal ready for delivery.*
(Mildred Cookson)

EPILOGUE

—

The Daydream

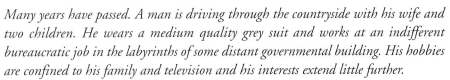

Many years have passed. A man is driving through the countryside with his wife and two children. He wears a medium quality grey suit and works at an indifferent bureaucratic job in the labyrinths of some distant governmental building. His hobbies are confined to his family and television and his interests extend little further.

The motor car that transports this family is of an approved Euro design. It has four seats, a small engine and sensors that keep it a regulation distance from the car in front and correctly placed within the confines of the roads. Between the day-glow stripes that ensure easy visibility to other traffic, the massive bar code on the roof for identification by hidden cameras in the event of a minor infringement of the law, and the flashing lights that activate should the driver exceed the speed limit, there are areas of paintwork. Like the lives of the occupants, it is grey.

The trees and hedges are iridescent with early autumn golds and browns. Someone in the car spies a movement some distance off the highway. It is a windmill, the sails rising and falling against the rural scene. The driver pulls onto the grass verge and everyone disentangles themselves from their safety seats and harnesses, to stand watching the timeless sight.

The driver remembers a passage in a book he once read when the protagonists in a great twentieth-century sea battle had to hold their fire while a majestic sailing clipper passed ghost-like between them. The windmill is a symbol of individuality. Each saw and chisel cut is the triumph not of a distant, buck-passing committee, but of a single individual. One mind, two hands and a tool well sharpened and skilfully held will produce a tough, effective work of art. Each piece of timber is a challenge, not to be forced into submission, but to be worked with to create something worthwhile. Like the sailing ship that held up the battle, the windmill has its own unique character.

"It must be hundreds of years old" says one of the children.

But it isn't.

At the end of the long private drive from the road is a group of eurocars not dissimilar to that on the grass verge. Their drivers have come to stay with their friend who owns the windmill and spend the weekend helping him grind both his own grain and that which they have brought in their cars.

The mill is a post mill, currently the most expensive type, for it is more exciting to run than a smock or a tower mill. Inside the buck there is good humour as a young woman goes upstairs to take her turn at hoisting wheat from the roundhouse. The sack chain rattles and the owner looks out from the stone floor to where the white patent sails pass one by one across his vision of fields and hedges and blue autumn sky.

The mill has cost him a lot of money. The European Union has long since put insurmountable bureaucratic barriers up against the building of new windmills, the "restoration" of one from the barest of remains being the only alternative to buying a fully restored example on the open market. He remembers the bidding at the auction, this mill project fetching more than some due to its complete roundhouse and the fact

Wimblehurst, nr Horsham, Sussex. *Note the tailpole fantail and petticoat between the body and the roundhouse.* (T.B. Pyne, author's collection)

that the original had been fitted with a fantail and current legislation only permitted mills to be re-erected when they were exact copies of the original.

He is a successful businessman, but his own work is in parts of his mill. Many of his friends having also contributed their skills in an attempt to leave their mark for posterity. He glances over to where the husband of the woman using the sack hoist is standing by the stairs. He made and handed over to the millwrights one of the bridgetrees on the floor below. It is a small thing amongst the mass of parts, but it is his bridgetree and will always be so, even long after he has passed away and his contribution has been forgotten.

The fly is on the move, taking her further round into a freshening breeze. The buck shudders and creaks, the sails flashing past the little window in the breast of the spout floor and the wheat stones giving out a high pitched rumble beneath their haze of flour dust.

The family from the car have come down the drive to ask if they may take a photograph. Someone shows them around, only the son having the courage to ascend to the swaying bin floor. After a while they leave for home, the son turning to look back as they make their way to the road. He has been inspired by the majestic, swaying structure and he knows that as soon as he is able he will take up the owner's invitation to make a return visit. On Monday he will see if there is a book on windmills in the library . . .

They take their seats in the car and leave for the town. Behind them the sails soar high into the evening sky, each rise a gesture on behalf of individuality and against monotonous conformity.

Stanton, Suffolk. *A lost age. Beam scales.*

Selected Bibliography

Anon., *The English Scene*. A & C Black, London, 1930.

Apling, Harry, *Norfolk Corn Windmills*. Norfolk Windmills Trust, 1984.

Batten, M.I., *English Windmills*, vol.1. Architectural Press, London, 1930.

Beatson, Robert, F.R.S.E., *Vertical and Horizontal Windmills – An Essay*. London 1798.

Brangwyn, Frank, and Preston, Hayter, *Windmills*. Bodley Head , London, 1923.

Brunnarius, Martin, *The Windmills of Sussex*. Phillimore, Chichester, 1979.

Buckland, Stephen, ed. Watts, Martin, *Lees' Patent Windmill*. S P A B, 1987.

Clarke, Allen, *Windmill Land*. J M Dent, London, 1916.

Coles Finch, William, *Water Mills and Windmills*. C W Daniel, London, 1956.

Coultard, Capt. and Watts, Martin, *Windmills of Somerset*. Research Publishing, London, 1978.

Darby, M.C., *The Draining of the Fens*. Cambridge University Press, London, 1956.

Dutt, William A., *The Norfolk Broads*. Methuen, London, 1903.

Farries, K.G. and Mason, M.T., *Windmills of Surrey and London*. Charles Skilton, London, 1966.

Farries, K.G., *Essex Windmills, Millers and Millwrights*. Charles Skilton, London, 1981.

Flint, Brian, *Suffolk Windmills*. Boydell Press, Woodbridge, 1979.

Foord Hughes, A., *Windmills in Sussex*. Walkers Galleries, London, 1930.

Freese, Stanley, *Windmills and Millwrighting*. Cambridge University Press, London, 1957.

Gregory, Roy, *East Yorkshire Windmills*. Charles Skilton, London, 1985.

Guise, Barry, *Windmills of Anglesey*. Attic Books, Wales, 1992.

Harrison, H.C., *The Story of Sprowston Mill*. Phoenix House, London, 1949.

Hemming, Rev. Peter, *Windmills in Sussex*. C W Daniel, London, 1936.

Irving, Lawrence, *Windmills and Waterways*. Heinemann, London.

Kent County Council, *Windmills in Kent*. Kent County Council, 1955.

Kershaw, J.C., *Wind, Tide and Stream*. Private, Gravesend, 1940.

Long, George, *The Mills of Man*. Herbert Joseph, London, 1931.

Mais, S.P.B., *England of the Windmills*. J M Dent, London, 1931.

Major, J.Kenneth, and Watts, Martin, *Victorian and Edwardian Windmills and Watermills*. Batsford, London, 1977.

Martin, Edward A., *Life in a Sussex Windmill*. Allen and Donaldson, London, 1920.

Paddon, J.B., *Windmills in Kent*. Maidstone, 1920.

Skilton, C.P., *British Windmills and Watermills*. Collins, London, 1947.

Smith, D., *English Windmills*. vol.2. Architectural Press, London, 1932.

Transactions of the Newcomen Society. *Various*.

Thurston Hopkins, R., *Old Watermills and Windmills*. Philip Allen, London.

Thurston Hopkins, R., and Freese, Stanley, *In Search of English Windmills*. Cecil Palmer, London, 1931.

Thurston Hopkins, R., *Old English Mills and Inns*. Cecil Palmer, London, 1927.

Wailes, Rex, *The English Windmill*. Routledge and Kegan Paul, London, 1954.

Wailes, Rex, *Windmills in England*. Architectural Press, London, 1948.

Ward, Owen, *French Millstones*. The International Molinological Society, 1992.

Wolf, Alfred R., *Windmills*. John Wiley, New York, 1885.

Woods, K.S., *Rural Crafts of England*. George G Harrap, London, 1949.

Glossary

Terms included in the text and other synonymous or useful expressions. Figures in italics are page references.

ANNULAR SAIL *A ring-like sail with radial shutters similar to a modern iron windpump*, 53.

APPOLD TURBINE *A type of pump driven by marsh mills*, 40

BACKSTAYS *Brace the sail frame from the stock*, 47.

BAY *The space between two sail bars*, 49.

BED STONE *The lower stationary mill stone*, 64.

BIN *Contains the grain in the upper floors of the mill*.

BIN FLOOR *Contains the grain bins*, 63.

BLUE STONE *Imported from Germany; one-piece mill stone*, 65.

BODY *Upper wooden part of a post mill*, 20.

BOLTER *Early type of flour-dresser*, 75.

BOLTING CLOTH *Cloth used in a bolter*.

BRAKE *Operates on the rim of the brake wheel to stop the sails*, 25, 48.

BRAKE LEVER *Actuates the brake*.

BRAKE ROPE *Enables the brake to be operated from any floor*.

BRAKE WHEEL *Largest gear wheel in the mill, situated on the windshaft*, 25.

BREAST *The front of the mill*, 24.

BREAST BEAM *Supports the neck bearing of the windshaft*, 24.

BRIDGE TREE *Supports the lower end of the stone spindle*, 69.

BRIDGING BOX *Adjustable stone spindle bearing on the bridge tree*.

BUCK *Suffolk post mill body*.

CANT POST *Corner post of a smock mill*.

CAP *The movable top of a smock or tower mill*, 29.

CAP CIRCLE *Circular sub-frame from which the cap rafters rise on some mills.*

CAP SHEERS *Main lengthways timbers of a cap.*

CLAMPS *Pass either side of a poll end to strengthen some stocks.*

CLASP ARM WHEEL *The arms form a square which grips the shaft*, 79.

CLOTH SAILS *The same as Common Sails.*

COCK HEAD *The rounded tip of the stone spindle*, 67.

COLLAR *Steadies the body of a post mill on the post*, 24.

COMMON SAILS *Early cloth-covered sails (cloth sails).*

COMPASS ARM WHEEL *The arms are mortised through the shaft*, 77.

COMPOSITE MILL *The body of a post mill is mounted on a short tower in the same way as a tower mill cap.*

COMPOSITION STONES *Manufactured from very hard chippings and cement*, 56.

CROSS *Alternative method to poll end for attaching the sails*, 52.

CROSSTREES *Cross over one another to form the bottom of a post mill trestle*, 22.

CROWNTREE *The main beam of a post mill body; carries the bearing upon which the whole mill turns*, 22.

CULLEN STONES *The same as Blue stones.*

CURB *The ring on top of a smock or tower mill body upon which the cap turns*, 31.

DAMSEL *Vibrates the shoe in an underdrift mill*, 70.

DEAD CURB *The cap skids round on iron or brass pads without the use of rollers.*

DOUBLE SHUTTERED SAILS *Shutters on both sides of the whip.*

DRESSER *General term for bolter or wire machine*, 75.

DRESSING *The furrows cut on the face of the stone*, 65.

DUST FLOOR *Floor just below the cap.*

EYE *The hole in the centre of the runner stone*, 64.

EYE STAFF *Short staff used for checking the level of the area around the eye*, 66.

FAN *A small set of sails positioned at right angles to the main sails*, 57.

FAN BRACES *Brace the fly posts from the cap.*

FAN SPARS *The same as fly posts.*

FAN STAGE *A stage at the rear of the cap to provide access to the fantail.*

FAN STAR *Iron hub of the fan*, 57.

FANTAIL *Turns the sails to face the wind automatically*, 57.

FLY POSTS *Upright posts which support the fan.*

FRENCH BURR *A built-up mill stone used for flour*, 64.

FURROWS *The main grooves in the grinding face of a mill stone*, 65.

GALLERY *Platform around the cap or tower of a smock or tower mill.*

GATE *A slide found in some shoes to restrict the flow of grain.*

GOVERNOR *Maintains the correct gap between the mill stones*, 69.

GRAIN CLEANER *Machine for cleaning grain*, 75.

GRAFT SHAFT *A wooden shaft to which an iron extension has been added.*

GREAT SPUR WHEEL *The large spur wheel which drives the stone-nuts*, 32, 79.

GRIST *Term for meal used for animal food.*

GUDGEON *Iron pin projecting from a shaft to form a bearing.*

HACKLE PLATE *Prevents dirt entering the bearing in the bed stone.*

HEAD-SICK *The mill leans forwards.*

HEAD WHEEL *Brake wheel.*

HEMLATH *Joins the tips of the sail bars*, 47.

HOLLOW POST MILL *The drive passes down through the post, and drives the machinery in the roundhouse*, 38.

HOPPER *Contains the grain just above the stones, on the stone vat.*

HORSE *Frame that supports the hopper and shoe.*

HURST *Frame in the breast of some Midlands post mills which carries the stones*, 70.

JACK STAFF *Used to check the vertical position of the stone-spindle*, 67.

JOG SCRY *Inclined trough with sieves in the bottom to grade flour.*

JUMPER *Jog Scry.*

LANDS *The raised parts between the furrows of a mill stone*, 65.

LANTERN PINION *Early type of bevel gear*, 77.

LATHS *Lengthways bars of a common sail.*

LEADING BOARD *On the leading side of a single-shuttered sail.*

LIVE CURB *The cap turns on rollers*, 31.

MACE *Driven by the quant or stone-spindle*, 67.

MEAL BIN *Receives the ground meal from the stones.*

MIDDLING *Kentish term for a stock.*

MILL BILL *Tool for dressing the stones*, 65.

MULTI-SAILED *A windmill with more than four sails.*

NECK *The bearing behind the poll end*, 25.

NECK BEARING *The neck of the windshaft turns on this*, 25.

OVERDRIFT *Stones driven from above.*

PATENT SAIL *The shutters are reefed from within the mill*, 49.

PEAK STONE *A one-piece millstone mined in England*, 64.

PETTICOAT *Vertical boarding around the lower part of a cap or post mill.*

PICK *Pointed mill bill used to dress the stones*, 65, 66.

PIERS *Take the weight of the crosstree ends*, 22.

PINTLE *The bearing at the top of the post*, 22.

PIT WHEEL *Drives the scoop wheel of a drainage mill.*

POLL END *Used to attach the sails on many mills (canister).*

POST *The body of a post mill turns on this*, 22.

POST MILL *The entire body turns on a main post*, 20.

PRICK-POST *Vertical beam in the breast of a post mill.*

PROOF STAFF *The staff is checked against this.*

QUANT *Drives the stones in an overdriven mill*, 67.

QUARTERBARS *Diagonal supports of the main post*, 22.

RACK *Gearing around the curb of a smock or tower mill*, 31.

RED OXIDE *Used on the staff to test the level of the stone face.*

RED STONE *Type of millstone used in the north-west.*

ROLLER-REEFING SAILS *These use roller blinds instead of the shutters of a patent sail,* 52.

ROUNDHOUSE *Building to protect and provide storage around the trestle of a post mill,* 27.

RUBBING BURR *Piece of hard stone used to rub off the high places of a millstone.*

RUNNER STONE *The upper revolving millstone,* 64.

SACK CHAIN *Raises sacks to the upper floors.*

SACK-HOIST *Used with sack chain,* 73.

SACK SLIDE *On some post mill ladders, used to lower sacks.*

SAILS *Utilise the wind-pressure to drive the machinery,* 47.

SAIL BACK *Strong sail whip used with a cross,* 52.

SAIL BARS *Crosswise bars of the sail frame,* 47.

SAMSON HEAD *Iron bearing fitted at bearing of post and crowntree.*

SCOOP WHEEL *Raises water on marshes to a higher level,* 39.

SHEER BEAMS *Pass fore and aft under the spout floor of a post mill,* 24.

SHOE *Feeds grain from the hopper into the eye of the stone.*

SHUTTERS *Open and close in the same manner as a Venetian blind in the bays of spring and patent sails.*

SHUTTER BAR *Connects the shutters.*

SIDE GIRT *On either side of a post mill these each take half the weight,* 24.

SINGLE-SHUTTERED SAILS *Have shutters on the trailing side only.*

SKIRT *The outer section of a millstone.*

SMOCK MILL *A wooden tower with a cap, which turns to face the wind,* 29.

SMUTTER *A type of vertical grain cleaner which removes a fungus from the grain.*

SPIDER *Operates the shutter bars of a patent-sailed mill,* 51.

SPRATTLE BEAM *Carries the upper bearing of the upright shaft. Also the upper bearings of the quants.*

SPRING SAILS *A shuttered type of sail controlled by a spring,* 49.

SPRING-PATENT SAILS *A rare type of patent sail which has a spring in the striking gear of each sail to provide individual regulation.*

STAFF *Used to test the surface of the stone for high spots,* 65.

STAGE *Gallery around a smock or tower mill.*

STAVES *The equivalent of teeth in a lantern pinion.*

STEELYARD *A long lever for tentering the stones, connected to the governor,* 69.

STOCK *The main timber which supports the sails when a poll end is used,* 47.

STONES *Grind the grain,* 63.

STONE CASING *Stone vat.*

STONE-DRESSING *The act of recutting the furrows in the grinding face of the millstone,* 65.

STONE FLOOR *The floor upon which the stones are situated.*

STONE-NUT *The gear that drives the stone,* 63.

STONE-SPINDLE *Supports the runner stone,* 67.

STORM HATCH *Allows access to the poll end from within the mill.*

STRIKING GEAR *Operates the shutters of patent sails,* 51.

STRIKING ROD *Passes from end to end of the windshaft to actuate the shutters of patent sails,* 51.

STUMP IRON *Pivot for triangles.*

SUBSTRUCTURE *Term for the trestle of a post mill.*

SUNK POST MILL *The trestle is buried in the ground,* 38.

SWEEP *Southern name for a sail.*

SWEEP-GOVERNOR *Device for regulating the speed of the sweeps.*

TAIL *The rear of a windmill.*

TAIL BEAM *Supports the tail bearing of the windshaft.*

TAILPOLE *Turns many early mills to face the wind.*

TAIL WHEEL *Smaller than the brake wheel, this drives the stones in the rear of a post mill,* 26.

TAIL WIND *A wind from behind the sails of a mill,* 26.

TALTHUR *The lever on the side of a post mill tailpole used to raise the ladder when turning the mill.*

TENTERING GEAR *General expression for the bridgetree, etc which are used for adjusting the gap between the stones.*

THRIFT *Handle which holds mill bills and picks,* 65.

TOLL *The taking of some flour or meal in payment for grinding.*

TOWER MILL *A windmill with a brick or stone tower and a cap which turns to face the wind,* 35.

TRESTLE *The sub-structure of a post mill.*

TRIANGLES *Cranks which operate the striking gear of patent sails.*

TRUCK WHEEL *Centres the cap of a tower or smock mill,* 31.

TRUNDLE WHEEL *Similar to a lantern pinion with the top flange removed and the staves shortened,* 77.

TWIST PEG *Adjusts the angle of the shoe.*

UNDERDRIFT *Stones driven from below.*

UPRIGHT SHAFT *The main shaft of a smock or tower mill which passes through several floors to drive the machinery,* 31.

VANE *Alternative name for shutter or fan blade.*

VAT *The casing which encloses the stones (tun),* 64.

WALLOWER *The bevel gear driven by the brake wheel when an upright shaft is used,* 31, 78.

WEATHER *The twist of a sail,* 47.

WEATHER BEAM *Alternative name for the breast beam.*

WHEEL-AND-CHAIN GEAR *Mechanism which turns the cap of some old smock and tower mills,* 29.

WHIP *The main timber of a sail when a sail stock is used,* 47.

WINDING *Turning the sails to face the wind.*

WINDSHAFT *The main axle of the sails,* 22, 24.

WIRE MACHINE *Type of flour dresser which uses wire mesh to grade the meal,* 75.

Y WHEEL *A wheel with Y-shaped forks around the rim which give the rope or chain increased grip,* 59.

Windmills to be Seen

ACCESS

Most windmills are privately owned and it is to be hoped that this will long be the case, for public organisations have a tendency to turn windmills into museums and to rationalise their surroundings (the idea of a tarmacadam public car park at Drinkstone makes one wince). Most private owners are more than willing to allow access to the true enthusiast, but it should be remembered that one is intruding into their personal lives. Each one of us is an ambassador for the others and access should be gained by writing, telephoning or asking politely at the door. Please avoid wandering about on privately-owned land, prying into a mill or its outbuildings without prior permission or behaving in any way that might be construed as rude.

Many grants are available to owners to maintain or restore their windmills and it is usual for the grantors to insist that the public should be allowed occasional access. Most owners have taken advantage of these grants at some time and a letter with stamped addressed envelope or a telephone call may gain access to an otherwise closed mill.

The Society for the Protection of Ancient Buildings has a windmill section which arranges trips to privately owned windmills. This is a good way to obtain access to obscure wind and watermills and offers the chance to meet other enthusiasts. Once a year there is a National Mills Day organised by the SPAB. This is usually in May and every windmill and watermill possible is open to the public.

The SPAB produces an excellent list and map of windmills and watermills that are open to the public, and it is recommended that those interested should apply to them for a copy.

The address of the SPAB is:- The Secretary, Wind and Watermill Section, SPAB, 37 Spital Square, London E1 6DY, United Kingdom.

A LIST OF SELECTED WINDMILLS

The purpose of this list is that of providing the reader who has no previous knowledge of windmills with the names of an interesting selection which are externally reasonably complete. Most of these have been restored and may be seen from the road. Many are privately owned and for this reason are not accessible to the public. This same ruling also applies to those in public ownership, for although most councils are quite willing to show people around, provided an appointment has been made, it is hardly fair for the casual visitor to bother them in this manner.

The original intention was that this section should cover all those counties which contain windmills, in approximately equal proportions. A preliminary survey of the situation, however, at once made it quite obvious that some counties contain far more restored windmills than others. A county like Kent, for instance, is bristling with restored mills, many of these being of excellent quality, and it would have been senseless to have excluded these just to keep the proportion equal to that of, say, Anglesey.

This is not a comprehensive list, but merely a suggestion of possible windmills to at least look at from the road. There are many good mills that have not come to mind, and many that are in full working order that I have been unaware of having been completed. There are other mills that I believe to be open to the public, but which may only be open for a few days each year.

Those mills marked * are believed, at the time of writing, to be open to the public.

Bedfordshire
Stevington   Post mill. Unusual roof shape.

Buckinghamshire
Brill   Post mill.
*Lacey Green   Restored smock mill of considerable age.
*Pitstone Green   Old post mill bearing date 1627.
Quainton   Restored tower mill.

Cambridgeshire
Barnack   Tower mill.
Burwell   Restored tower mill. Working order.
Great Chishill   Restored post mill. Open trestle. Ladder fantail.
Great Gransden   Restored post mill. Open trestle.
Over   Working tower mill.
Six Mile Bottom   Restored post mill.
*Soham   Octagonal tower mill. Working order.
*Swaffham Prior   Restored tower mill. Working.
*Wicken Fen   Small pumping smock mill. Working order.
Willingham   Smock mill. Worked to 1960s. Part restored.

Six Mile Bottom, Cambridgeshire. *A clockwise post mill shown in the early 1960s before renovation.*

Capenhurst, Cheshire.
As it stood in 1958, before restoration.

Willaston, Cheshire.
The cap and wheel-and-chain winding gear are typical of the North-east. The cleats for holding the chain and brake rope while at work are still visible above the stage.

Cheshire	
Bidstone	Restored tower mill.
Capenhurst	Restored tower mill.
Willaston	House-converted tower mill.
Derbyshire	
Dale Abbey	Post mill. Restored. Worked into the 1950s.
*Heage	Six-sailed tower mill. Restored.
Essex	
Aythorpe Roding	Restored post mill. Working order.
Bocking	Post mill restored in 1930s.
*Mountnessing	Restored post mill. Working order.
Ramsey	Post mill. Moved from Suffolk. Had roof fantail.
*Rayleigh	Restored tower mill.
*Stanstead Mountfitchet	Restored tower mill.
*Thaxted	Restored tower mill. Working order.
*Upminster	Restored smock mill.
Hampshire	
*Burseldon	One of the rare Hampshire windmills. Working order.
Herefordshire	
Leinthal Starkes	New smock mill. Private.
Hertfordshire	
Arkley	Tower mill.
Cromer	Restored post mill that has the most westerly application of the ladder fantail.

Margate, Kent.
Draper's Mills in 1889.
W. Wrigglesworth,
author's collection.

Isle of Wight

*Bembridge	Restored tower mill with wheel-and-chain winding gear.

Kent

Chillenden	Preserved post mill with open trestle.
*Cranbrook	Restored smock mill with incorrect sails. Working order.
*Herne	Restored smock mill. Working order.
*Margate	Restored smock mill. Working order.
*Meopham	Restored smock mill.
Rolvenden	Post mill without ladder.
*Sandwich	Restored smock mill.
*Sarre	Restored smock mill. Working and authentic.
*Stelling Minnis	Smock mill. The last windmill to work in Kent. Working order.
*West Kingsdown	Renovated smock mill.
*Willesborough	Restored smock mill. Working order.
*Wittersham	Post mill. Restoration to working order planned.
*Woodchurch	Completely rebuilt smock mill.

Margate, Kent.
Draper's Mills in 1960, before restoration to working order during the 1970s.

Lancashire

Lytham	Tower mill.
*Thornton	Tower mill. Renovated for visitors.

Sandwich, Kent. *About 1960, before restoration was commenced by Vincent Pargeter.*

Wrawby, Lincolnshire. *The restored post mill turning.*

Leicestershire

Kibworth Harcourt	Post mill.

Lincolnshire

*Alford	Five-sailed tower mill. Working.
*Boston	Restored tower mill. Working.
*Burgh-le-Marsh	Restored clockwise tower mill. Can be seen working.
*Heckington	Tower mill with eight sails. Original and in working order.
*Kirton-in-Lindsey	Restored tower mill. Working.
*Lincoln	Restored tower mill. Working order.
*Sibsey	Six-sailed tower mill. Working order.
Swineshead	Tower mill.
*Waltham	Tower mill with six sails. Worked to late 1950s. Working order.
*Wrawby	Restored post mill. Mostly new, but interesting.

Billingford, Norfolk.
Shortly after working for the last time in the late 1950s.

London
*Brixton   Restored tower mill.

Norfolk
*Berney Arms   Drainage mill. Restored. Very tall.
Billingford   Restored tower mill. Last mill to work in the county.
Burnham Overy   Tower mill.
*Denver   Restored tower mill. Working order.
Garboldisham Common Post mill under restoration. The last post mill in Norfolk. Ladder fantail.
Great Bircham   Restored tower mill. Working order.
Horsey   Restored drainage mill.
Paston   Tower mill. Restored.
Stracey Arms   Restored pumping mill.
*Sutton   The second tallest windmill in England. A tower mill. In process of restoration.
Thrigby   Post mill. New mill being built.
Thurne   Pumping mill. Restored.
*Wicklewood   Restored tower mill.

Nottinghamshire
*Sneinton, Nottingham	Green's mill, rebuilt in the 1980s.
*North Leverton	Tower mill. Working. Has never been restored.
Tuxford	Restored tower mill.

Oxfordshire
Great Hazely	Tower mill with stocks for three sails.

Shropshire
Asterly	Restored tower mill. Not open to the public. Will eventually be working.
Weston	Derelict tower mill. Very important mill that is the only remaining linseed oil crushing windmill in England.

Somerset
Ashton	Restored tower mill. Last windmill to work in the county.
High Ham	Tower mill with thatched cap, once a speciality of the area.

Weston, Shropshire. *Now very derelict, this is the only remaining mill for crushing oil from linseed. It seems appalling that this important mill is not being restored.*

Suffolk

*Bardwell	Restored tower mill. Works with engine.
Drinkstone	Post mill worked to the 1970s, making it the last to do so in England. The second pair of windmills.
Framsden	Restored post mill.
Friston	The finest remaining post mill in the world. Last worked in 1959. Under restoration.
Herringfleet	Pumping smock mill. Capable of work.
Holton	Restored post mill.
Pakenham	Tower mill. Has never been restored. Working until late 1970s.
St Olaves	Small pumping smock mill.
*Saxtead Green	Completely restored post mill. Turns but does not work.
Stanton	Restored post mill. Working order. To be restored to full work.
*Thelnetham	Restored tower mill. Working order.
Thorpness	Post mill. Moved early 1920s to pump water.
*Woodbridge	Restored tower mill. Working order.

Surrey

*Outwood	Very old post mill. Working order.
Reigate Heath	Post mill.
*Shirley	Restored tower mill.
Tadworth	Post mill without sails.
*Wimbledon Common	Rebuilt in 1890s as a landmark.
Wray Common	House-converted tower mill.

Sussex

Argos Hill	Restored post mill with tailpole fan.
*Chailey	Smock mill.
*Clayton	One of only two remaining pairs of windmills in England. Restored post mill which works regularly. Tower mill yet to be returned to work.
Cross-in-Hand	The last post mill to work in the county. Being restored. Tailpole fantail.
*High Salvington	Restored post mill. Working order.
Icklesham	Post mill with roof fantail. Under restoration.
Keymer	Post mill last worked 1912. Demolished 1995. Being rebuilt with new materials.
*Nutley	Restored post mill.
Patcham	The last windmill built in the county in 1885. The last of the 28 windmills of Brighton. House-converted.
*Polegate	Restored tower mill in working order. Worked with engine into 1960s.
Punnetts Town	Very prominent smock mill. Renovated, but not very authentic.

Cross-in-Hand, Sussex. *As it stood in 1970 after losing a sail while at work.*

*Shipley	Smock mill of quite late date. Working order.
Stone Cross	Tower mill. Worked to mid 1930s. To be restored to working order.
*West Blatchington	Six-sided smock mill. Part restored.
West Chiltington	House-converted smock mill.

Warwickshire
Chesterton — Very unusual tower mill. Working order.

Wiltshire
Wilton — Tower mill. Restored.

Worcestershire
*Avoncroft — Post mill. May be seen working. In Museum of Rural Life.

Yorkshire
Holegate — Tower mill.
*Skidby — Tower mill. The last to work in the county. Now restored. Working order.

Stone Cross, Sussex. *As it stood in the 1950s. It had last worked in about 1936.*

Overleaf: **Preesall, Lancashire**. *A fine photograph showing the mill in its working days. Note the typical black cap and sails, the latter with strong weather and tapering towards the tip.* (Mildred Cookson)

INDEX

Preesall, Lancashire. *The mill staff. John Thornton, foreman, on the right. Left, Matt Bradshaw who later took over the position of foreman and was the last miller.* (Mildred Cookson)